METHUEN'S MONOGRAPHS
ON BIOCHEMICAL SUBJECTS

━━━━

General Editors:

Sir Rudolph Peters F.R.S. and F. G. Young F.R.S.

Nucleotides and Coenzymes

Nucleotides and Coenzymes

D. W. HUTCHINSON Ph.D.
University Chemical Laboratory, Cambridge

LONDON: METHUEN & CO LTD

Contents

General Editors' Foreword

Methuens' Biochemical Monographs are similar in form and aim to the series of Methuen's Monographs on other subjects. The volumes can be regarded as chapters of a large work which records progress in biochemistry in general. Each volume in the series aims to provide an authoritative survey of the present position in a particular field of biochemistry by an expert in the subject, written in such a way that the book can provide an introduction both for the student who is reaching the end of his undergraduate studies and for the research worker who wishes to have an account of a subject cognate with his own. Although these accounts of the subject are intended for those who wish to study biochemistry, in practice the books have proved to be attractive to a much wider group.

The books are intended to be handy and to be rather more than a review but less than a detailed monograph. No attempt has been made to include a complete bibliography, but references are given which should provide a key to the essential relevant literature.

As biochemistry widens its interests so the diversity of the subjects included in this series will grow. They naturally range from some which are primarily chemical in their emphasis to those which are essentially biological in their outlook.

The present book by Dr D. W. Hutchinson is primarily chemical in its range. It is a companion book to Professor Davidson's *The Biochemistry of the Nucleic Acids*, which has now run through several editions. The enormous extension of the literature in the field of Nucleic acids due to the activity in research, has made it essential to discuss the more chemical side in a separate volume. This Dr Hutchinson's monograph succinctly does, always with a view to the biochemical importance of the substances under discussion.

Preface

This book is intended as a companion to the Methuen Monograph *The Biochemistry of the Nucleic Acids* by Professor J. N. Davidson and in it the chemistry and biochemistry of nucleosides, mono- and polynucleotides, nucleotide coenzymes, and the two 'non-nucleotidic' coenzymes, pyridoxal phosphate and thiamine pyrophosphate, will be described.

It is obvious that an exhaustive and detailed review of a subject of this nature would be beyond the scope of a Methuen Monograph (and probably beyond the scope of the author). If a more detailed treatment is required of certain aspects of the subjects which are dealt with, I would refer the reader to one of the following excellent, and more extensive, works: *The Nucleic Acids* edited by Chargaff and Davidson, *The Enzymes* edited by Boyer, Lardy, and Myrbäck, and *The Chemistry of the Nucleosides and Nucleotides* by Michelson.

The field is reviewed up to the end of September 1963, but one of the necessary evils of producing a book of this kind is that some of the statements made in it may be out of date by the time of publication. This is particularly true of the subject of protein biosynthesis which is discussed at the end of Chapter 5, as this field is expanding rapidly at the present time.

Throughout, I have attempted to use the nomenclature for co-enzymes and enzymes which is approved by the International Union of Biochemistry. Thus, I have used nicotinamide-adenine dinucleotide (NAD^+ and its reduced form NADH) instead of diphospho-pyridine nucleotide or Coenzyme I. I have, however, symbolized inorganic orthophosphate and inorganic pyrophosphate as P_i and PP_i respectively in descriptions of biochemical reactions for which the ionic forms of the ortho- and pyrophosphate are not defined.

In addition, a shorthand nomenclature for oligo- and poly-nucleotides has been adopted. The nucleosides are represented by their initial capital letters, e.g. A for adenosine and T for thymidine. Assuming a $3' \rightarrow 5'$ linkage by a phosphate residue between the nucleosides, the phosphate residue may be represented by the suffix p, and the polynucleotide may be built up from the 5' hydroxyl end in the following manner. Adenylyl $(3' \rightarrow 5')$ adenosine is represented by ApA, adenylyl $(3' \rightarrow 5')$ adenosine-3' phosphate by ApAp, and the 5' phosphate of adenylyl $(3' \rightarrow 5')$ adenosine by pApA. Deoxynucleo-sides are represented by the prefix d, and oligodeoxynucleotides are represented as follows, deoxycytidylyl $(3' \rightarrow 5')$ deoxycytidine is d-CpC.

I have used abbreviations for the Journals which are approved by the Chemical Society of London, except that the following shortened forms have been employed:

Journal of the Chemical Society	*JCS*
Journal of the American Chemical Society	*JACS*
Journal of Biological Chemistry	*JBC*
Biochemical Journal	*BJ*
Biochimica et Biophysica Acta	*BBA*
Proceedings of the National Academy of Sciences (Washington)	*PNAS*

The series *The Enzymes* Volumes I to VIII edited by Boyer, Lardy and Myrbäck which is published by the Academic Press is referred to in the following manner, *The Enzymes* (1962), **6**, 301.

I would like to thank Messrs Macmillan for permission to use the diagram of the Watson–Crick helical form of DNA on p. 122.

I should like to thank Professor Lord Todd for his interest in this book and Drs V. M. Clark, J. F. P. Richter, and S. G. Warren for their kindness in helping me to prepare this volume. Not least I should like to thank Sir Rudolph Peters and Professor F. G. Young without whose encouragement this book would never have been written. The award of an Imperial Chemical Industries Research Fellowship is gratefully acknowledged.

D. W. HUTCHINSON

Cambridge 1963

CHAPTER ONE

Historical Introduction

The discovery of the first nucleotide, inosinic acid, by Liebig in 1847 (1), preceded the discovery of nucleic acids by Miescher (2) by some twenty years.

Liebig isolated inosinic acid from extracts of meat along with creatine and sarcosine, but unfortunately he did not detect the presence of phosphorus in inosinic acid. The correct structure was not established until 1911 when Levene and Jacobs (3) proved that it was the 5′ phosphate ester of hypoxanthine riboside.

Miescher (2) obtained a material with a high phosphorus content from the nuclei of pus cells which he had treated with pepsin and dilute hydrochloric acid. On the addition of ether to the digests of the pus cells, a material which Miescher called 'nuclein' was precipitated from the reaction mixture. Nuclein was insoluble in organic solvents and acids but was readily soluble in alkali. A most remarkable feature about nuclein was its high phosphorus content as lecithin was the only naturally occurring organo-phosphorus compound which had been discovered at that time. Hoppe-Seyler, to whom Miescher presented his results for publication, was sceptical about the nature of nuclein and refused to publish until he and two of his students had repeated Miescher's experiments (4).

Altmann, who continued Miescher's work after the latter's death, was the first to introduce the term 'nucleic acid' (5). Altmann obtained protein-free nucleic acid from yeast as well as animal tissues. Shortly afterwards, Kossel and Neumann (6) discovered a nucleic acid in thymus glands.

The second stage in the development of the chemistry of nucleic acids, the elucidation of the components of the nucleic acids, was begun by Piccard who isolated guanine and hypoxanthine from sperm nuclei. The determination of the constituents of nucleic acids was continued mainly by Kossel and Levene, and by 1914 all the main purine and pyrimidine bases together with D-ribose had been identified. The existence of two distinct types of nucleic acid was apparent when the nucleic acid from yeast on hydrolysis yielded adenine, guanine, cytosine, and uracil together with orthophosphate and D-ribose, whereas the nucleic acid from thymus glands gave adenine, guanine, cytosine, and thymine together with orthophosphate and a pentose. This pentose was later identified as 2-deoxy D-ribose. These nucleic acids came to be called ribonucleic and deoxyribonucleic acids and it was assumed that ribonucleic acid was the component of plant tissues and deoxyribonucleic acid was the component of animal tissues. This sweeping assumption was finally disproved by the histochemical studies of Brachet (7), and by the analytical studies on cells of Davidson and Waymouth (8).

Although the structures of most of the nucleosides and nucleotides had been determined by 1940, the study of nucleosides and nucleotides did not progress rapidly until the introduction of paper chromatography (9), paper electrophoresis (10), and ion exchange chromatography (11). These techniques enable small quantities of nucleosides and nucleotides to be separated and identified unequivocally as a routine operation. This is an enormous improvement on 'classical' separation techniques involving precipitation and crystallization, as it is almost impossible to separate chemical compounds with very similar properties by such methods.

The first nucleotide coenzyme was reported by Harden and Young in 1906 (12) as the heat stable cofactor of alcoholic fermentation; this coenzyme is now known as nicotinamide-adenine dinucleotide (NAD^+). Some years then elapsed until the discovery of other coenzymes such as adenosine triphosphate (13) and nicotinamide-adenine dinucleotide phosphate (14); here again the numbers and diversity of nucleotide coenzymes were not realized until the introduction of paper and ion exchange chromatography. This was largely due to the extreme lability of the coenzymes under the conditions of 'classical' isolation techniques.

The chemical synthesis of nucleosides and nucleotides, which was begun by Levene, has been developed by Todd, who together with his co-workers, has been responsible for the rigorous structural proof and synthesis of many nucleosides, nucleotides, and coenzymes. The synthetic approach to nucleotide chemistry has been continued by Khorana who has synthesized polynucleotides and such complex coenzymes as Coenzyme A (15).

After the determination of the ratios of the base pairs adenine + thymine and guanine + cytosine in DNA by Chargaff (16), and the demonstration by Brown and Todd that the 3'- and 5'-hydroxyls of successive nucleosides in RNA and DNA were joined by a phosphodiester group, the way was open for Watson, Crick, and Wilkins (18) to demonstrate the helical coil structure of DNA.

The biological role of nucleic acids and the nucleotide coenzymes has been demonstrated at a much later date than the elucidation of their structure. In 1944, Avery, MacLeod, and McCarty (19) showed that the 'transforming principle', which under suitable conditions could transform one type of pneumonococcus bacterium into another, was DNA and hence DNA must have some effect on the genetic structure of cells. This discovery was followed by others on the mode of action of bacteriophages. These consist in the main of nucleoprotein, and when the bacterial cell becomes infected by the phage, the DNA separates from the nucleoprotein and enters the cell (20) to direct the synthesis of DNA and proteins which are alien to the host cell. Additional evidence concerning the genetic role of nucleic acids was provided by Fraenkel–Conrat (21) and Schramm (22) from a study of the tobacco mosaic virus (TMV). The genetic information in TMV, which is a ribonucleoprotein, lies exclusively in the RNA component of the virus.

Another biological function of RNA is the direction of the biosynthesis of protein; this subject is discussed in detail in the final section of Chapter 5 of this volume. Once RNA had been implicated in the biosynthesis of protein, the question arose as to how the RNA could 'code' amino acids into specific positions in the protein. This led to the development of the theory of the triplet code for the transference of genetic information (23). In this theory, three successive nucleosides in the RNA code for one specific amino acid. There has recently been a great burst of activity throughout the world in an effort to crack the triplet code as to which three nucleosides (or more particularly which three bases) code for which amino acid.

To summarize, the discovery of the nucleic acids and coenzymes was followed by the determination of their structure, and structural determination methods were simplified by the introduction of such modern analytical techniques as paper and ion exchange chromatography, together with ultraviolet and infrared spectroscopy. This development in analytical procedures has been followed by considerable effort to try to discover the exact biological function of nucleic acids and nucleotide coenzymes. Thus the arbitrary boundaries between organic and biochemistry have been broken down and the study of nucleotides and nucleic acids could perhaps best be described as a 'molecular science' rather than any particular branch of chemistry.

REFERENCES

1. LIEBIG (1847), *Annalen*, **62,** 317.
2. MIESCHER (1871), *Hoppe-Seyler's Med. chem. Untersch.*, 441.
3. LEVENE and JACOBS (1911), *Ber.*, **44,** 746.
4. PLOSZ (1871), *Hoppe-Seyler's Med. chem. Untersch.*, 461; LÜBAVIN, *loc. cit.*, 463; HOPPE-SEYLER, *loc. cit.*, 486.
5. ALTMANN (1889), *Arch. anat. u. Physiol. Physiol. Abt.*, 524.
6. KOSSEL and NEUMANN (1894), *Ber.*, **27,** 2215.
7. BRACHET (1940), *C. R. Soc. Biol. Paris*, **133,** 88.
8. DAVIDSON and WAYMOUTH (1944), *BJ*, **38,** 39.
9. MARKHAM and SMITH (1951), *BJ*, **49,** 401.
10. MARKHAM and SMITH (1952), *BJ*, **52,** 552.
11. COHN (1950), *JACS*, **72,** 1471.
12. HARDEN and YOUNG (1906), *Proc. Roy. Soc. B*, **78,** 369.
13. FISKE and SUBBAROW (1929), *Science*, **70,** 381.
14. WARBURG and CHRISTIAN (1931), *Biochem. Z.*, **242,** 206.
15. KHORANA and MOFFATT (1961), *JACS*, **83,** 663.

16. CHARGAFF (1955), *The Nucleic Acids*, Vol. I, eds. Chargaff and Davidson, Academic Press, N.Y., p. 350.
17. BROWN and TODD (1952), *JCS*, 52.
18. WATSON and CRICK (1953), *Nature*, **171**, 964.
19. AVERY, MACLEOD, and MCCARTY (1944), *J. Exptl. Med.*, **79**, 137.
20. HERSHEY and CHASE (1952), *J. gen. physiol.*, **36**, 39.
21. FRAENKEL-CONRAT (1956), *JACS*, **78**, 882.
22. SCHRAMM and GIERER (1956), *Nature*, **177**, 702.
23. CRICK, BARNETT, BRENNER and WATTS-TOBIN (1961), *Nature*, **192**, 1227.

CHAPTER TWO

Nucleosides and Nucleotides

2.1 Introduction

Nucleosides can be defined as compounds in which a purine or pyrimidine base is linked glycosidically to a carbohydrate. Phosphate esters of nucleosides are called nucleotides. Nucleotides, the sub-units of nucleic acids, are also the constituents of various important coenzymes.

2.2 Occurrence

The most important source of nucleosides and nucleotides are the nucleic acids which can be degraded to nucleosides and nucleotides by either chemical or enzymic methods.

Nucleic acids normally occur in association with proteins, such aggregates being known as nucleoproteins. Very mild isolation techniques are necessary to separate the nucleoprotein from cell tissue and to prevent denaturation of the nucleic acid portion of the nucleoprotein. For example, denaturation of the nucleic acid takes place if the nucleoprotein is subjected to heat, acid, alkali or even to the excessive use of high-speed mincers during isolation. A common technique for the isolation of nucleic acids is the extraction of the nucleoprotein and cell tissue with solutions of salts at low ionic strength or phenol, followed by separation of the nucleic acid from the nucleoprotein by means of anionic detergent (1, 2). This procedure gives nucleic acids of differing molecular weight and these have been fractionated by chromatography on either ion-exchange celluloses (3), or ion-exchange resins (4); or by counter-current distribution (5).

Chromatography on columns of cross-linked polysaccharide (Sephadex) (6) appears to be a very satisfactory method of isolating nucleic acids. The Sephadex column removes low molecular weight electrolytes from solutions of the nucleic acid, enabling the nucleic acid to be separated into homogeneous fractions. Using Sephadex, bacterial RNA has been separated into ribosomal RNA and transfer-RNA (7); and aminoacyl transfer-RNA's have been separated from ATP and the amino acid.

Even using these mild isolation methods there is no rigid proof that the nucleic acid has not decomposed on isolation as normal chemical criteria of purity cannot easily be applied to *in vivo* systems.

Acid hydrolysis of nucleic acids liberates the purine bases since purine-sugar bonds are much more labile in acid than are pyrimidine-sugar bonds. Hydrolysis can be effected with alcoholic or aqueous acid, and Levene has shown that the purine-sugar bond is split at pH 2 before an appreciable amount of inorganic phosphate is produced (8, 9). Pyrimidines are liberated only after vigorous treatment with acid and some decomposition of the bases may take place at the same time.

Since the purine-sugar bond is comparatively stable in the presence of strong alkali, RNA can be hydrolysed under these conditions to orthophosphate, and purine and pyrimidine nucleosides (10); nucleotides can be isolated if milder conditions are employed (11). Chemical methods of hydrolysis are unsatisfactory for DNA, as the purine nucleotides are removed in acid to leave 'apurinic' acid. Further degradation of 'apurinic' acid with acid does, however, liberate pyrimidine deoxynucleotides. Under the conditions required for alkaline hydrolysis, complete deamination of the purines and cytosine occurs (12). Enzymic hydrolysis has been used for the preparation of deoxyribonucleotides, and digestion of DNA from calf pancreas with deoxyribonuclease gives a good yield of the nucleoside-5′ phosphates (13, 14). Hydrolysis of RNA with ribonuclease gives ribonucleoside-2′,3′ cyclic phosphates and nucleotides which terminate in pyrimidine ribonucleoside-3′ or -2,3′ cyclic phosphates (15, 16).

When ribonucleoside-5′ phosphates are obtained from RNA by the action of snake venom phosphodiesterase, pyrimidine nucleoside 2′,5′- and 3′,5′-diphosphates and purine nucleosides are also produced (17). The enzymic hydrolysis of polynucleotides is described in more detail in Chapter 5.

The bases, nucleosides, and nucleotides produced by the hydrolysis of nucleic acids may most conveniently be identified, separated, and isolated by column chromatography. Both ion-exchange resins (18) and ion-exchange celluloses (19) have been used.

2.3 D-Ribose

Hydrolysis of RNA with acid gave D-ribose (I) (20, 21), which was identified from differences between physical constants of the sugar and other known pentoses, as D-ribose was unknown at the time of isolation.

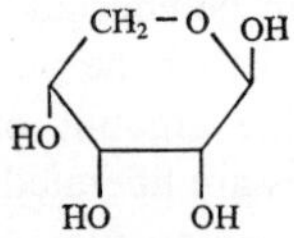

(I)

D-Ribose was first synthesized by the epimerization of D-arabonic acid to D-ribonic acid followed by the reduction of the lactone of D-ribonic acid to give D-ribose. The original synthesis from D-arabinose has been improved and, for example, D-arabinose (II) can be converted into D-ribose by the action of hydrogen peroxide on the intermediate D-arabinal (III) (24).

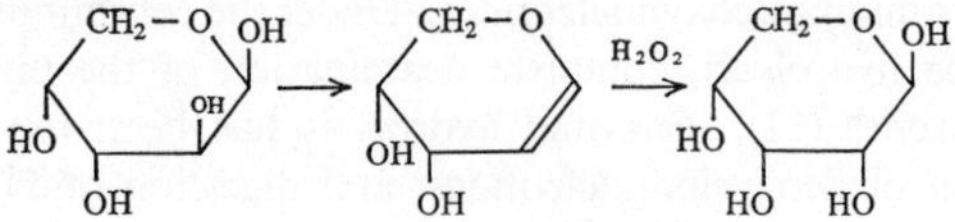

(II)　　　　　(III)　　　　　(I)

Ribonucleic acids from many different sources have been subjected to hydrolysis; but, so far, only D-ribose has been isolated as the sugar component. It is, therefore, generally assumed that this is the only sugar present in RNA.

2.4 Deoxy-D-ribose

The carbohydrate component of thymonucleic acid was first isolated by Levene and London (24) who degraded thymus DNA enzymically to the purine nucleosides and prepared the deoxy sugar, 2-deoxy-D-ribose (IV), from these purine nucleosides (25). Levene and London were unable to isolate a sugar from the pyrimidine nucleosides, as the drastic conditions needed to cleave the pyrimidine-sugar bond caused the sugar to decompose to levulinic acid. The isolation of deoxynucleosides has been improved by the introduction of ion-exchange chromatography and 2-deoxy-D-ribose has been prepared by the acidic hydrolysis of purine nucleosides (26). Several syntheses of the sugar have been reported (27–30), for example, D-arabinal (III) has been converted into 2-deoxy-D-ribose by the addition of water to the carbon-carbon double bond with dilute sulphuric acid at low temperature (28).

2-Deoxy-D-ribose (31) like D-ribose (32) is in the pyranose form in the solid state.

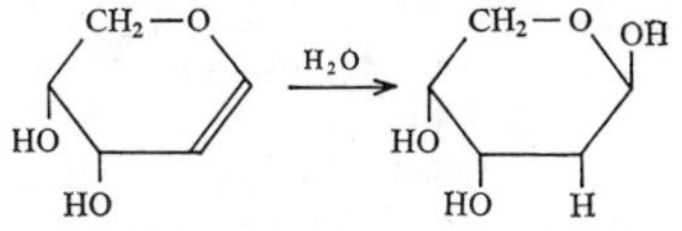

(III)   (IV)

2-Deoxy sugars are much more reactive than their oxygenated counterparts, and are readily converted to O- and N-glycosides. Deoxy sugars are sensitive to acid and, for example, treatment with acid will degrade 2-deoxy-D-ribose to levulinic acid.

From paper chromatographic examination of hydrolysates of DNA, obtained from many different sources, Chargaff (33) has concluded that 2-deoxy-D-ribose is the only sugar present in DNA.

2.5 Pyrimidine bases

The three main pyrimidine bases which occur in nucleic acids are uracil (V), thymine (VI), and cytosine (VII). Several pyrimidine bases

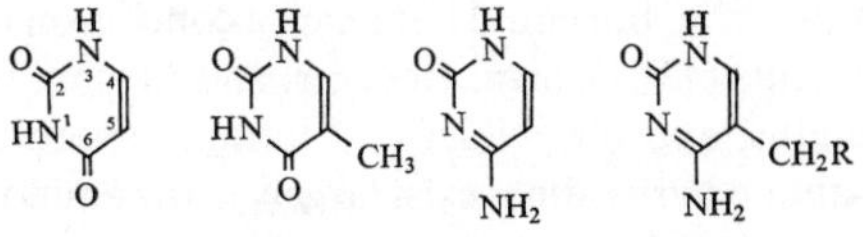

(V)   (VI)   (VII)   (VIII)

2

are minor components of DNA and RNA. For example, 5-methyl cytosine (VIII, R = H) is a minor component of both DNA and RNA (34, 35) and 5-hydroxymethyl cytosine (VIII, R = OH) replaces cytosine completely in the DNA of 'T even' phages (36, 37).

The isolation, proof of structure, and synthesis of uracil, thymine and cytosine are reviewed by Levene and Bass (38) and will not be considered here.

Synthesis. In general, the pyrimidine ring system may be synthesized from a derivative of urea and an activated three-carbon fragment. For example urea and malic acid in the presence of fuming sulphuric acid condense to give uracil (39).

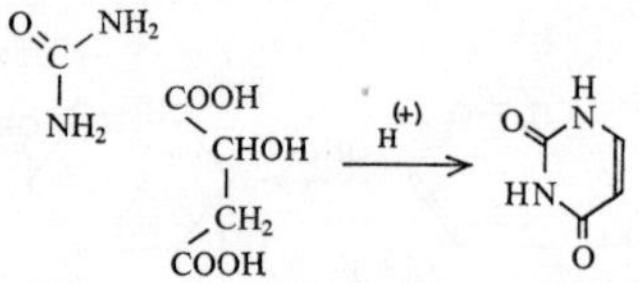

Thymine may be prepared in an analogous manner from urea and 3-methyl malic acid.

Properties. The pyrimidine ring shows some similarities to pyridine in its chemical behaviour (40, 41). Thus the 2-, 4-, and 6-positions are electron deficient, and the 5-position exhibits 'normal' aromatic reactivity. However, the only property which will be considered here is the keto-enol tautomerism of the hydroxy and amino groups. This has an important influence on the hydrogen bonding between bases which is required by the Watson and Crick double helical structure of DNA (42).

From a study of ultraviolet spectra of 2- and 6- substituted pyrimidines, Marshall and Walker concluded that the hydroxy group exists in the keto form, but could not reach a conclusion in the case of amino substituents (43). Brown, Hoerger, and Mason, from a study of basic strengths, and ultraviolet and infrared spectra, concluded that 2- and 6-amino pyrimidines exist largely in the amino, as opposed to the imino, form (44). Kenner, Reese, and Todd have also shown that for cytosine the amino group predominates (45). X-ray crystallographic examination of thymine (46, 47), cytosine (46, 48), and uracil (49) confirms their structures.

2.6 Purine bases

The main purine bases which occur in both RNA and DNA are adenine (IX) and guanine (X).

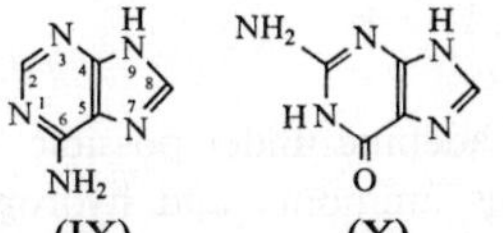

(IX)   (X)

In the past few years, however, several other purine bases have been isolated from RNA in trace amounts, including 2-methyl adenine, 6-methylamino purine, 6,6-dimethylamino purine, 1-methyl guanine, 6-hydroxy-2-methylamino purine (50), and 6-hydroxy-2-dimethyl-amino purine (51).

The isolation and identification of adenine and guanine are described by Levene and Bass (52), who also describe the proof of structure of their deamination products, hypoxanthine (XI) (from adenine) and xanthine (XII) (from guanine).

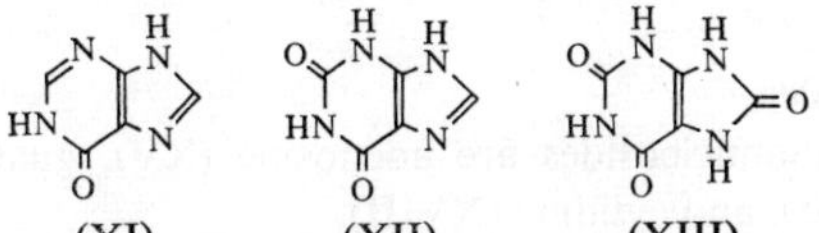

(XI)   (XII)   (XIII)

Synthesis. The final proof of structure of the purines was their synthesis, and after Fischer's early work on the synthesis of uric acid (XIII) (53) Traube discovered a more versatile method when he condensed a 4,5-diamino pyrimidine with a simple carbonyl compound such as formic acid. Thus guanine was synthesized from 2,4,5-triamino-6-hydroxy pyrimidine and formic acid (54, 55).

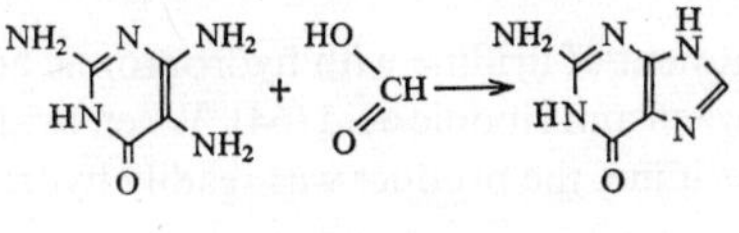

In vivo, imidazole ribose phosphates are precursors of adenine, guanine and hypoxanthine nucleotides (56) and the synthesis of purines from imidazole derivatives has been achieved *in vitro* from 4-amino imidazole-5-carboxamides (XIV) and ortho-esters (57).

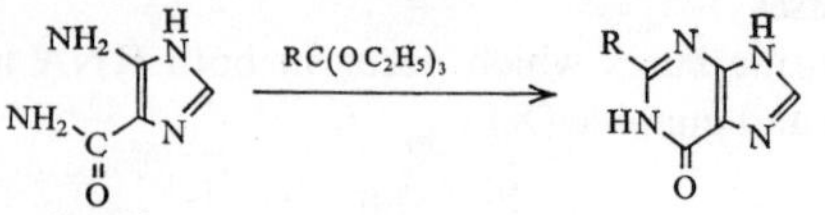

(XIV)

The formation of adenine under possible 'primitive earth' conditions from aqueous ammonia and hydrogen cyanide has been reported. 4-Amino imidazole-5-carboxamide (XIV) has been isolated from the reaction mixture, suggesting that the imidazole ring has been formed before the pyrimidine ring (58).

Properties. From their infrared and ultraviolet spectra, Mason has concluded that hydroxy purines, like hydroxy pyrimidines, exist in the keto form and so the structures of guanine (X), hypoxanthine (XI), xanthine (XII), and uric acid (XIII) are as shown above (59). From similar evidence the amino group appears to be in the amino, as opposed to the imino, form for purines and their ribo- and deoxyribo-nucleosides (60, 61).

2.7 Nucleosides

The main ribonucleosides are adenosine (XV), guanosine (XVI), uridine (XVII), and cytidine (XVIII).

The main deoxyribonucleosides are deoxyadenosine (XIX), deoxyguanosine (XX), deoxycytidine (XXI), and thymidine (XXII).

The first ribonucleoside to be isolated was vernine (62) which was later renamed guanosine (XVI) by Levene and Jacobs, who also isolated a nucleoside containing adenine, which they called adenosine (XV) (63). Adenosine and guanosine may be deaminated to inosine (XXIII) and xanthosine (XXIV) respectively.

Structure. Treatment of uridine with hydrobromic acid and bromine gave 5-bromouracil and ribonic acid (64). When uridine was reduced to 4,5-dihydrouridine, the product was readily hydrolysed by acid to

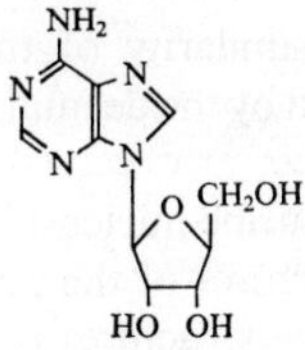

(XV)

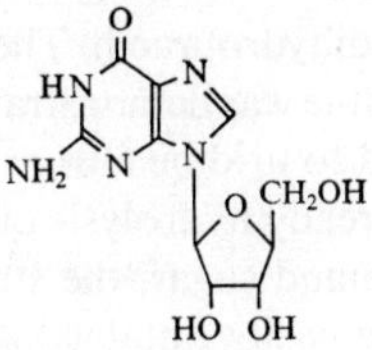

(XVI)

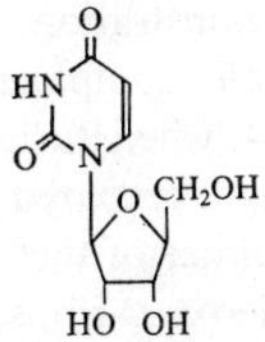

(XVII)

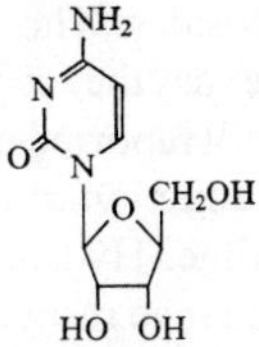

(XVIII)

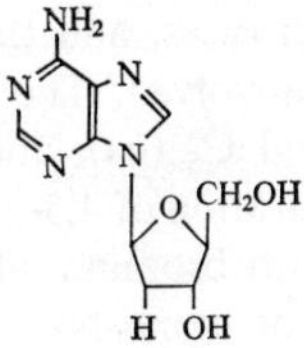

(XIX)

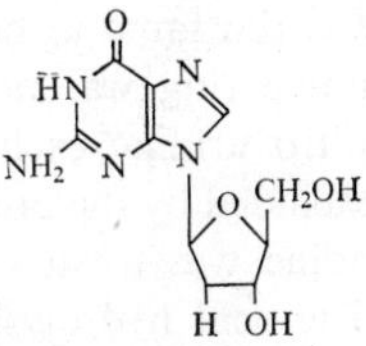

(XX)

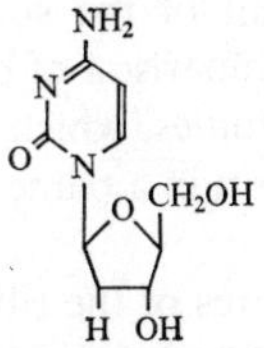

(XXI)

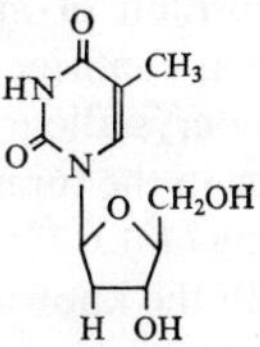

(XXII)

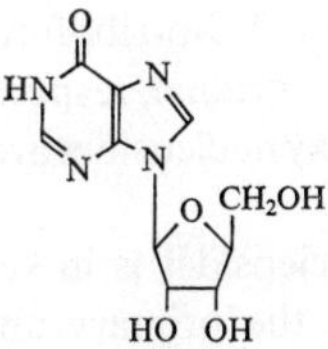

(XXIII)

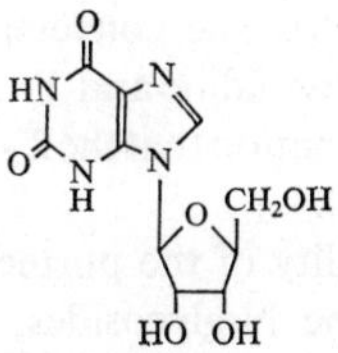

(XXIV)

ribose and 4,5-dihydrouracil. The similarity of the structures of cytidine and uridine was demonstrated by the deamination of cytidine with nitrous acid to uridine (10).

Owing to the ready hydrolysis of purine nucleosides in acid to the component base and sugar, the structures of the purine deoxyribonucleosides were easily obtained. The structures of the pyrimidine deoxyribonucleosides were tacitly assumed to be analogous to those of the ribonucleosides. The first demonstration of the presence of 2-deoxy-D-ribose as the carbohydrate component of pyrimidine nucleosides was not reported until 1954, when Burke adapted Levene's method for the reduction of uridine and prepared dihydrothymidine and dihydrocytidine. Hydrolysis of either of these compounds with an acidic ion-exchange resin gave 2-deoxy-D-ribose (65).

From the evidence of the deamination of cytidine to uridine, Levene concluded that the position of attachment of the sugar to the pyrimidine was the same in both cases, and that the position C_6 in the pyrimidine ring was not involved. The preparation of 5-bromo and 5-nitro uridine excluded C_5 (64), and the positions C_4 and C_5 were excluded by the preparation of 4,5-phenylhydrazino uridine when uridine was treated with bromine and then phenylhydrazine (66). The acid hydrolysis of mono-N-methyl uridine to 1-methyl uracil left only the N_3 position vacant for the glycosidic link (67). The position of attachment of the sugar to N_3 of the pyrimidine ring was confirmed by comparison of ultraviolet spectra (68) and by X-ray crystallographic studies, which also showed that the sugar ring was in the furanose form in a plane at right angles to the pyrimidine ring (48).

By analogy with the known structures of the ribonucleosides, the sugar in the deoxy series was assumed to be attached to the pyrimidine ring at N_3, and this postulation was confirmed by ultraviolet spectroscopy (68). The conversion of 3-β-D-ribofuranosyl thymine and uridine to thymidine and 2'-deoxy uridine, respectively, provided chemical confirmation that the 2'-deoxy nucleosides are N_3 substituted pyrimidines (69).

The acid lability of the purine nucleosides is in keeping with the properties of the N-glycosides, but the primary amino groups in adenosine (XV) and guanosine (XVI) are not involved, as they can be removed with nitrous acid to yield inosine (XXIII) and xanthosine (XXIV) respectively. This leaves four positions for attachment of the sugar to the purine, N_1, N_3, N_7 and N_9, of which N_1 and N_3 may be excluded as the methylation of xanthosine (XXIV) yields theophylline riboside (XXV) (70).

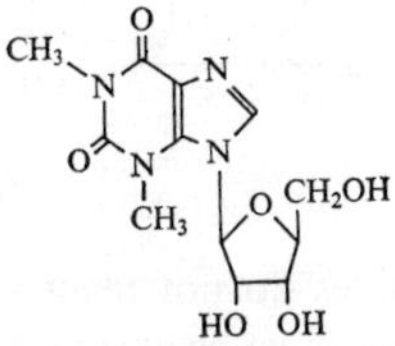

(XXV)

Since the ultraviolet spectra of adenosine and guanosine closely resembled that of 9-methyl adenine but were very different from that of 7-methyl adenine, it was concluded that the sugar was attached to N_9 (71). The purine deoxyribonucleosides had similar ultraviolet spectra to the ribonucleosides, and it was concluded that they too were N_9-glycosides (72). Chemical confirmation of the N_9-glycosidic structure was provided by the synthesis of adenosine (73). X-Ray crystallographic studies confirmed these conclusions, and again the sugar was shown to be in the furanose form in a plane at right angles to the purine (48).

The ring size of the ribose in ribonucleosides was established as furanose in the following manner. Adenosine was acetylated and then methylated; deacetylation of this product followed by acidic hydrolysis gave 2,3,5-trimethyl ribose (XXVI). The same trimethyl ribose was isolated after a similar series of reactions on guanosine. Oxidation of 2,3,5-trimethyl ribose gave 2,3,5-trimethyl ribonolactone (XXVII) which on further oxidation gave *meso*-dimethoxy succinic acid (XXVIII) (74).

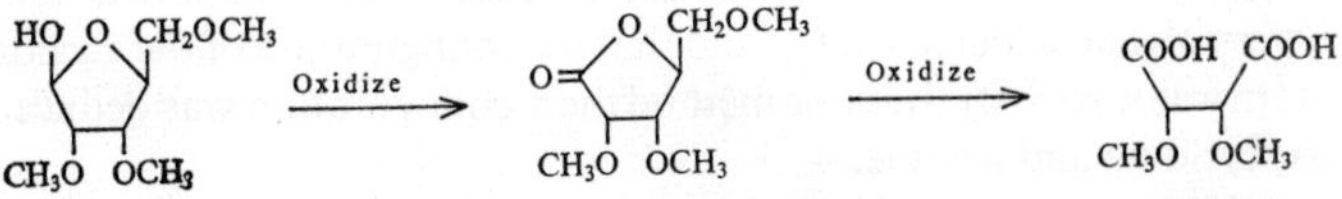

(XXVI)   (XXVII)   (XVII)

Titration with metaperiodate confirmed the furanose structure of the ribonucleosides. Since the 2′ and 3′-hydroxyl groups are on adjacent carbon atoms, one equivalent of metaperiodate is consumed to produce a dialdehyde (XXIX) but no formic acid (75).

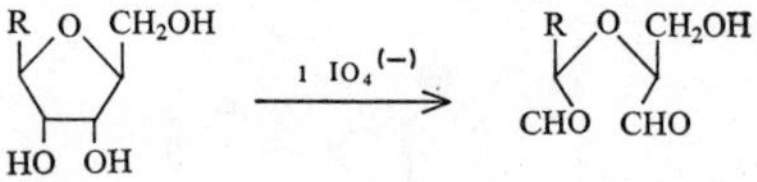

(XXIX)

The deoxyribonucleosides do not react with metaperiodate, and hence the *cis*-glycol system must be absent. From this, it follows that the sugar must be in the furanose form as a *cis*-glycol would be present in the pyranose form (76).

The structures and conformations of the sugars in nucleosides and nucleotides have been determined by nuclear magnetic resonance spectroscopy and agree with the general structures described above (77).

The configuration of the anomeric centre $(C_1′)$ of the natural ribonucleosides was also established by the action of metaperiodate. The oxidation product of adenosine (XXX, R = adenine) and 9-glucopyranosyl adenine (XXXI, R = adenine) was the same dialde-

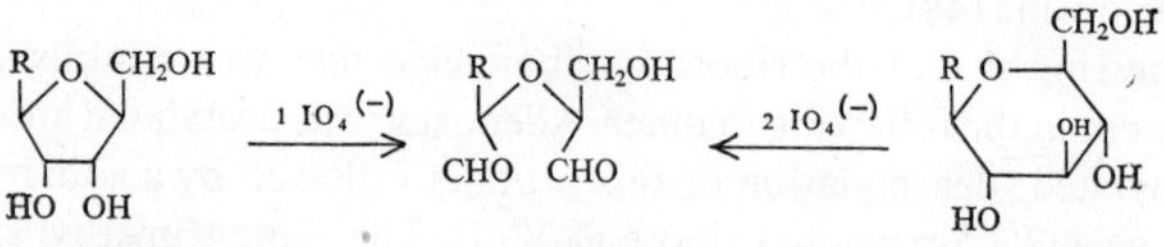

(XXX)   (XXIX)   (XXXI)

hyde (XXIX, R = adenine). In contrast to adenosine, the gluco-pyranosyl adenine consumed two equivalents of metaperiodate and formic acid was liberated (78). Since the glucopyranosyl adenine had been prepared from α-acetobromoglucose it was assumed that inversion had occurred at $C_1′$ and that the configuration of the carbon atom was now $β$. By the same method the $β$-configuration was deduced for cytidine and uridine.

Additional chemical proof of the $β$-configuration of the base-sugar bond came from the structure of cyclonucleosides (79). $2'$, $3'$-Isopropylidene adenosine (XXXII) was treated with p-toluene sulphonyl chloride, and the product was isomerized on heating to an ionic compound with the C_5' of the sugar attached to N_3 of the purine (XXXIII), This can only occur when the glycosidic link has the β-configuration.

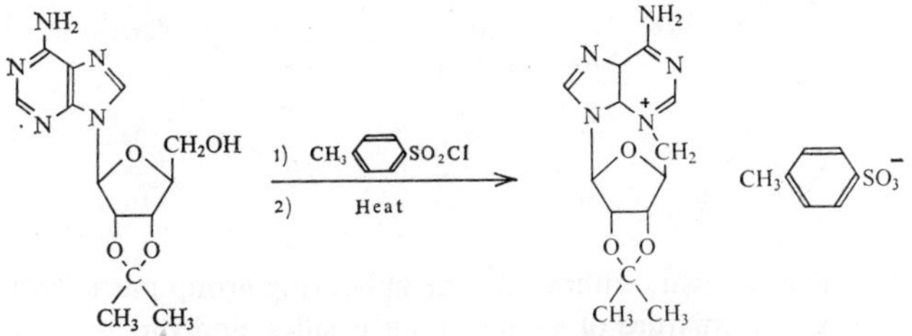

(XXXII)　　　　　　　　(XXXIII)

Similar cyclonucleosides have been prepared from cytidine, uridine, and thymidine, though in these cases the C_5' of the sugar is linked to the pyrimidine through the oxygen atom at C_2 on the pyrimidine.

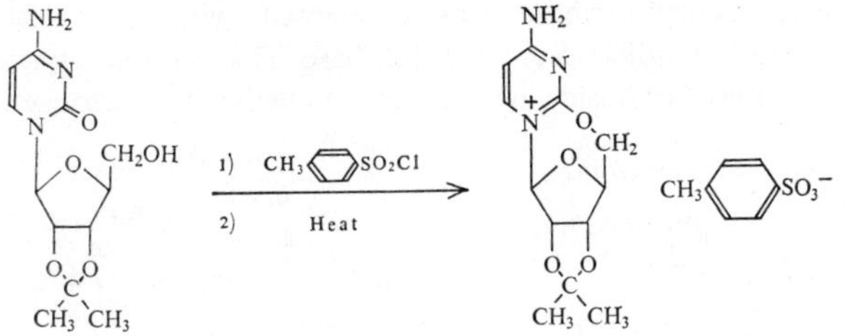

Synthesis. Purine glycosides can be prepared by the reaction between a heavy metal salt of a purine and an acetohalogeno-sugar (80, 81). A study of the stereochemistry of nucleoside synthesis has been provided by Baker (82) who found that, in general, condensation of a heavy metal salt of a purine or pyrimidine with an acetohalogeno sugar would yield a nucleoside with the groups on C_1' *trans* to those on C_2', regardless of the original configuration at C_1' and C_2'.

Since, for steric reasons, the large purine molecule is likely to attack the sugar from the side opposite to the acetyl group on $C_{2'}$, a double inversion of configuration must occur. A likely mechanism is displacement of the halogen as halide by the $C_{2'}$ acetyl group to give a cyclic ion which could then be attacked by the purine to give the nucleoside.

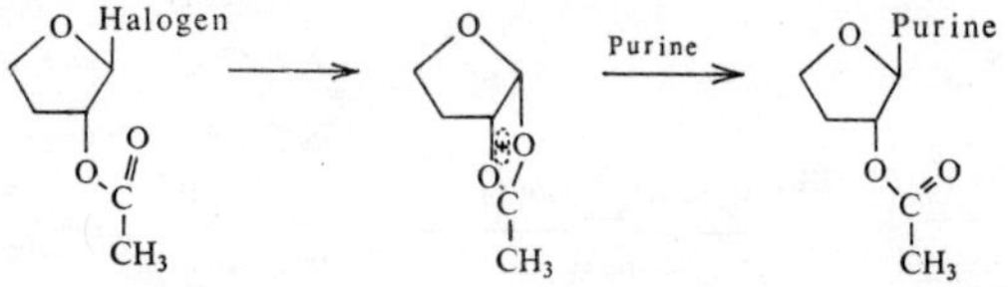

A 2'-deoxy sugar, without this neighbouring group participation, should give a mixture of α- and β-nucleosides, and this was found when 3,5-di-p-nitrobenzoyl 2-deoxy-D-ribofuranosyl chloride was condensed with mercuri-adenine (83). This synthetic method has been applied to the synthesis of deoxyadenosine (84), deoxyguanosine (84), deoxycytidine (85) and thymidine (86).

The synthesis of adenosine from a pyrimidine was conclusive proof of the position of attachment of the sugar to the purine (73). 2,3,4-Triacetyl-5-benzyl-D-ribose was condensed with 4,6-diamino-2-methylthiopyrimidine to give a Schiff base. This was deacetylated to give the glycofuranoside which was coupled with diazotized 2,5-

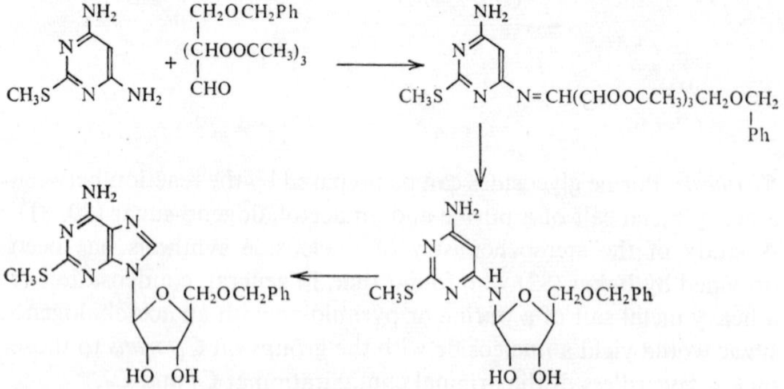

dichloro-aniline. The coupled product was acetylated, reduced to the amine, thioformylated, and then cyclized to the purine. The 2-methylthio and 5′-benzyl groups were then removed by hydrogenolysis with Raney nickel, and subsequent deacetylation gave adenosine identical with that obtained from natural sources (73).

Pseudouridine. Ion-exchange chromatography of either alkaline or enzymic hydrolysis products of yeast RNA gave a small amount of an unusual nucleotide (87, 88). The nucleotide could be hydrolysed to a nucleoside, containing uracil and ribose, isomeric with uridine.

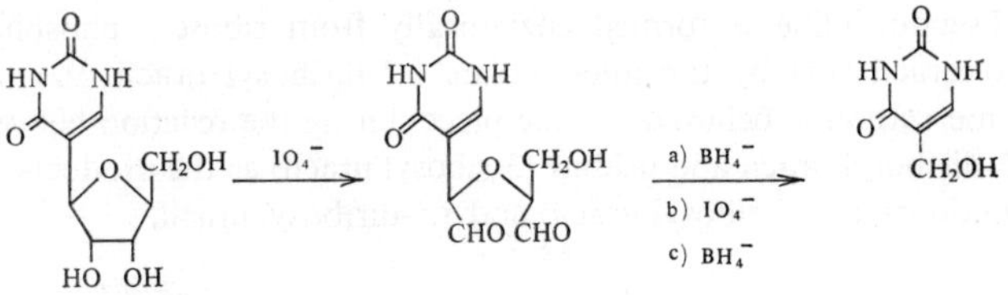

(XXXIV)

The ultraviolet spectrum of the nucleoside was similar to 5-hydroxymethyl uracil rather than uridine. The nucleoside consumed one equivalent of metaperiodate to give a dialdehyde but not formic acid, hence the ribose was present in the furanose form. Reduction of the dialdehyde with borohydride followed by further oxidation with

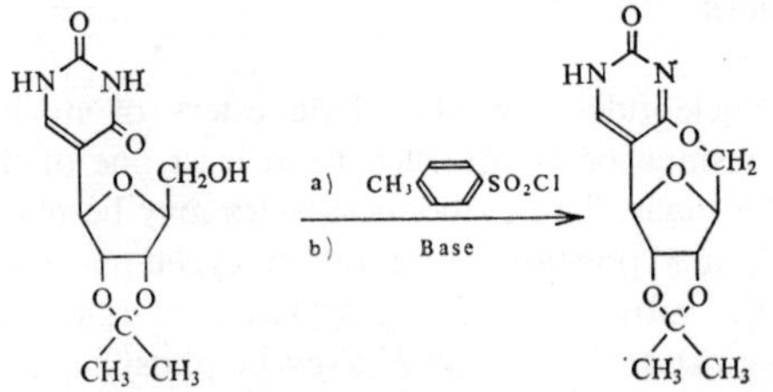

periodate gave an aldehyde which could be reduced to 5-hydroxymethyl uracil. Thus the nucleoside which has been given the trivial name pseudouridine was probably 5-ribosyl uracil (**XXXIV**).

The nuclear magnetic resonance spectrum confirmed the structure, as there was no signal which could be ascribed to the proton on C_5.

The configuration of the glycosidic uridine-ribose link was shown to be β by the formation of the cyclic nucleoside from pseudouridine (89). Isopropylidene pseudouridine (XXXV) was treated with p-toluene sulphonyl chloride then with base to give the cyclonucleoside (XXXVI), this can only happen with a β configuration at the glycosidic bond.

Pseudouridine has been synthesized from 2,3,5-tribenzoyl-D-ribofuranosyl chloride and the lithium derivative of 2,4-dimethoxy pyrimidine (90).

Pseudouridine is formed enzymically from ribose-5 phosphate and uracil (91) by the intermediate 3,5-diribosyl uracil (92). An isomerization is believed to take place during the reaction between 3,5-diribosyl uracil and uridine (3-ribosyl uracil) as the products are pseudouridine (5-ribosyl uracil) and 3,5-diribosyl uracil.

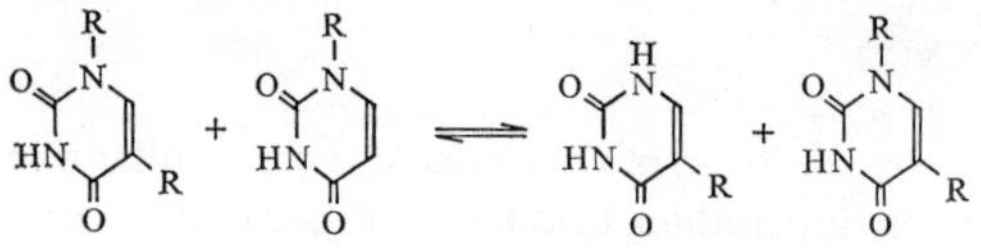

(where R = D-ribofuranosyl)

2.8 Nucleotides

Structure. Nucleotides are phosphate esters of nucleosides, the phosphoryl residue being attached to at least one of the hydroxyl groups of the sugar. Thus, ribonucleosides may be phosphorylated on the 2′, 3′, or 5′ positions. In addition, cyclic phosphates may be formed by the subsequent phosphorylation of a second hydroxyl group, giving rise to 2′, 3′- and 3′,5′-cyclic phosphates. Deoxyribonucleosides, on the other hand, can be phosphorylated only on the 3′ and 5′ positions and a cyclic 3′,5′-ester has been reported. Nucleoside polyphosphates such as adenosine di- and triphosphates will be described in a later chapter.

Examples of the different isomers of nucleoside monophosphates are given below.

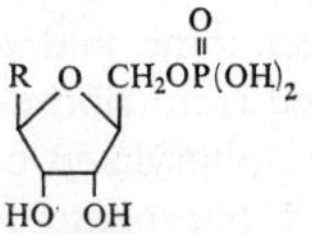

Ribonucleoside-5′
phosphate

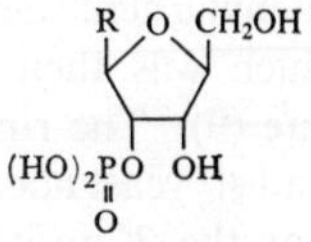

Ribonucleoside-2′
phosphate

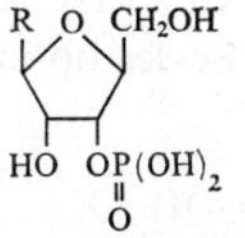

Ribonucleoside-3′
phosphate

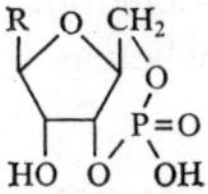

Ribonucleoside-3′,5′
cyclic phosphate

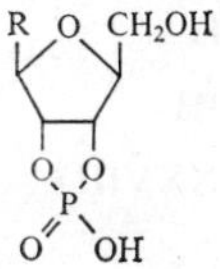

Ribonucleoside-2′,3′
cyclic phosphate

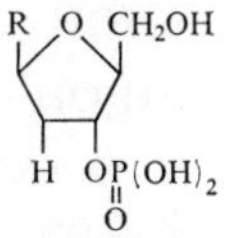

Deoxyribonucleoside-3′
phosphate

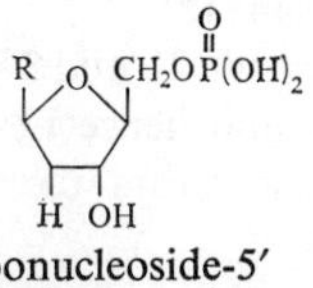

Deoxyribonucleoside-5′
phosphate

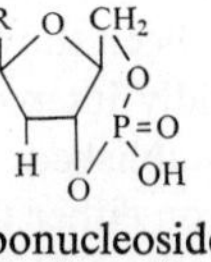

Deoxyribonucleoside-3′,5′
cyclic phosphate

The first nucleotide to be discovered, inosinic acid, was isolated by Liebig in 1847 (93). Liebig did not detect any phosphorus in this compound, and it was not until 1911 that this was identified as the 5′-phosphate ester of hypoxanthine riboside (21) by Levene and Jacobs.

Levene assumed that there were two distinct types of adenine nucleotides, depending on whether they were isolated from the RNA of yeast or muscle (94) and he demonstrated the location of the phosphate residue for yeast adenylic acid in the following manner. Yeast adenylic acid was deaminated with nitrous acid to an inosinic acid, which was then hydrolysed to hypoxanthine and a ribose phosphate (9). The ribose phosphate differed from ribose-5 phosphate, and so yeast adenylic acid must be phosphorylated on either the 2'- or the 3'-positions. Since this ribose phosphate could be reduced catalytically to optically inactive ribitol phosphate, it was assumed that the phosphoryl residue was located on the 3'-position in the nucleotide, as ribitol-3 phosphate (XXXVII) is optically inactive whereas the 2-isomer (XXXVIII) possesses optical activity (9).

$$
\begin{array}{ll}
\begin{array}{l}
CH_2OH \\
| \\
CHOH \quad O \\
| \qquad \| \\
CH-O-P{<}^{OH}_{OH} \\
| \\
CHOH \\
| \\
CH_2OH \\
\end{array}
&
\begin{array}{l}
CH_2OH \quad O \\
| \qquad \| \\
CH-O-P{<}^{OH}_{OH} \\
| \\
CHOH \\
| \\
CHOH \\
| \\
CH_2OH \\
\end{array} \\
\quad (XXXVII) & \quad (XXXVIII)
\end{array}
$$

The ribose phosphate obtained from guanylic acid was assumed to be identical with that from adenylic acid, thus guanylic acid was assumed to be the 3'-phosphate of guanosine (8).

It has been shown, however, that nucleoside 2'- and 3'-phosphates are rapidly interconvertible in acid (95), and hence Levene's work only established that yeast adenylic acid bears the phosphoryl residue on either the 2'- or 3'-position.

Carter and Cohn isolated, by ion-exchange chromatography of RNA hydrolysates, two isomers of adenylic acid which they named the 'a' and 'b' forms (96). The isomers were readily interconvertible and were stable to metaperiodate and hence were probably the 2'- and 3'- phosphates (97). Hydrolysis of adenylic acid 'a' with an ion-exchange resin in the acidic form gave ribose-2 phosphate (98), and ribose-3 phosphate was obtained after a similar hydrolysis of adenylic acid 'b'. The identity of the ribose phosphates was established by their reduction to the ribitol phosphates described above.

Muscle adenylic acid was shown to be adenosine-5′ phosphate in the following manner. Inosinic acid was produced after treatment of muscle adenylic acid with nitrous acid. Hydrolysis of inosinic acid gave ribose-5′ phosphate this was identified by oxidation to ribonic acid phosphate which was identical with a synthetic sample from ribose-5 phosphate; muscle adenylic acid consumed one equivalent of metaperiodate and hence must be adenosine-5′ phosphate (99).

Synthesis. Adenosine-5′ phosphate (AMP) has been synthesized in low yield from 2′,3′-isopropylidene adenosine and phosphorus oxychloride (100). Phosphorus oxychloride is a reactive phosphorylating agent but as it contains three labile phosphorus-chlorine bonds several products are obtained during the phosphorylation reaction. Diesters of phosphorochloridic acid are better phosphorylating agents than phosphorus oxychloride as they contain only one reactive phosphorus-chlorine bond and the protecting groups can be removed after the phosphorylation step. Ribonucleoside-5′ phosphates can be prepared in high yield from dibenzyl phosphorochloridate and the appropriate 2′,3′-isopropylidene nucleoside, the protecting groups being removed by hydrogenolysis in acidic solution (101–103).

An alternative method for the synthesis of nucleotides from nucleosides is by the use of carbodiimides (104). A carbodiimide can react with a phosphomonoester to produce an imidoyl phosphate which then breaks down to the urea and the phosphorylating species which is a trimetaphosphate.

Carbodiimides are not the only class of compounds which can form imidoyl phosphates, and ketenimides (105), isocyanates (106), cyanamides (107) and nitriles (108) all give imidoyl phosphates when treated with monoesters of phosphoric acid.

If a phosphomonoester containing a labile ester group is used in conjunction with carbodiimide, suitably protected nucleosides can be converted into nucleotides without difficulty. A phosphomono-ester which has been used extensively for this purpose is β-cyanoethyl phosphate (109), as the β-cyanoethyl moiety is removed from the product by mild alkaline treatment. For example this method has been used to prepare thymidine-3′ and -5′ phosphates, guanosine-5′ phosphate, deoxyadenosine-5′ phosphate and a variety of oligo-nucleotides phosphorylated on either the 3′ or 5′ positions (104, 109).

Deoxyribonucleoside-3′ phosphates can be readily prepared by the phosphorylation of the nucleoside protected in the 5′ position by a trityl or similar group. The unambiguous synthesis of ribonucleoside-2′ and -3′ phosphates is more difficult owing to the rapid intercon-version of these esters under common synthetic conditions.

A mixture of ribonucleoside-2′ and 3′ phosphates can be prepared by the phosphorylation of 5-trityl adenosine by the phosphoro-chloridate method, and the isomers separated by ion exchange chromatography (110).

Ribonucleoside-3′,5′ di-acetates have been prepared by the fusion of a mixture of the ribonucleoside-2′,3′,5′ tri-acetate and the ribo-nucleoside-5′ acetate (111) and uridine-2′ phosphate was synthesized by the phosphorylation of 3′,5′-di-acetyl uridine with dibenzyl phosphorochloridate. The protecting benzyl groups were removed before deacetylation in order to avoid attack by the neighbouring 3 -hydroxyl group on the fully esterified phosphate.

Ribonucleoside-3′ phosphates can be prepared by the action of ribonuclease on a cyclic 2′,3′-phosphate (112), but no specific chemical synthesis has been reported.

The ribonucleoside-2′ and -3′ phosphates are readily inter-convertible in acid, and the interconversion proceeds through the cyclic 2′,3′-phosphate (95). Attack by the neighbouring hydroxyl groups on either of the ribonucleoside-2′ or -3′ phosphates gives the cyclic phosphate.

Neighbouring group participation is a property common to all phosphomonoesters of *cis*-glycols which cyclize readily in alkali. The formation

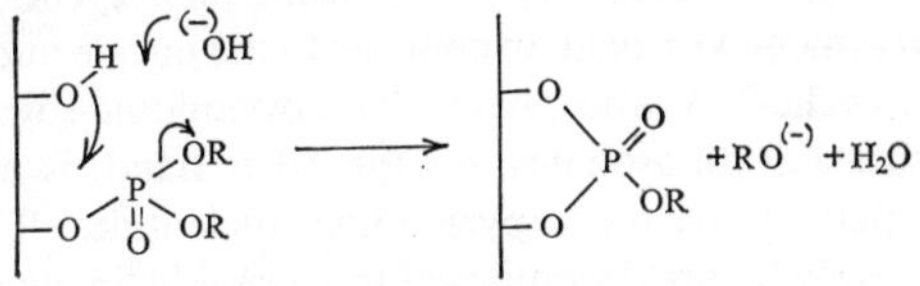

of ribonucleoside-2′, -3′ phosphates and 2′,3′-cyclic phosphates when RNA is hydrolysed in alkali is an example of this reaction (113).

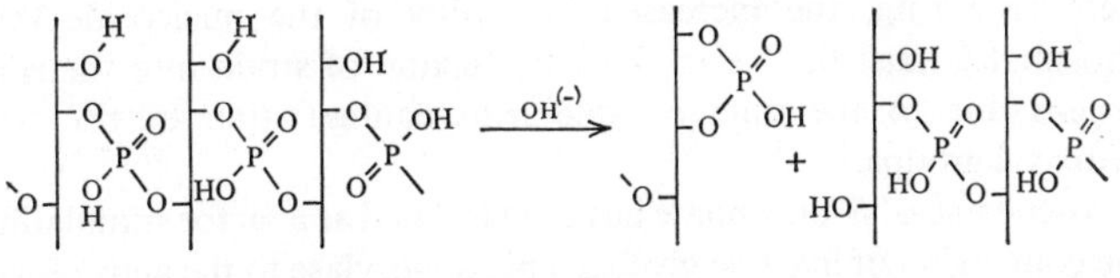

Cyclic phosphates in a five-membered ring are more alkali labile by a factor of 10^6 than those in six- or seven-membered rings (114, 115). The reason for this difference in stability is probably ring strain, as the existence of ring strain in cyclic phosphates with five-membered rings has been demonstrated thermochemically (116).

Cyclic ribonucleoside-2′,3′ phosphates can be prepared in high yield from either the ribonucleoside-2′ or -3′ phosphates and a dehydrating agent such as dicyclohexyl carbodiimide (117), or trifluoroacetic anhydride (110).

Despite the unfavourable *trans*-configuration of the hydroxyl groups; nucleoside-3′,5′ cyclic phosphates have been isolated from natural sources (118, 119). Adenosine-3′,5′ cyclic phosphate has been prepared by the degradation of adenosine triphosphate with barium hydroxide (120). The cyclic-3′,5′ phosphates of adenosine, uridine,

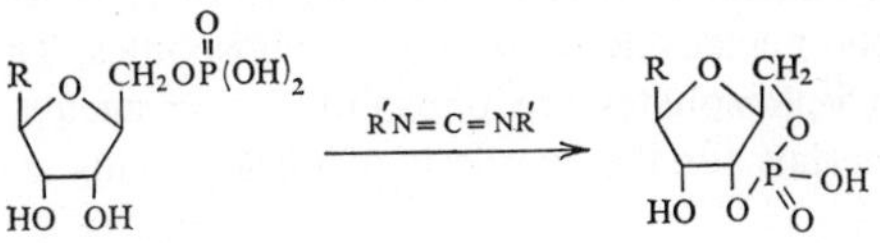

3

cytidine, guanosine, and thymidine have all been prepared by the action of dicyclohexyl carbodiimide on the nucleoside-5′ phosphate (121).

The purines are released very slowly from their cyclic-3′,5′ phosphates on treatment with acid, in contrast to the purine nucleoside-2′, -3′, -5′, and cyclic-2′,3′ phosphates. The pyrimidine-sugar bond of the nucleoside-3′,5′ phosphates, on the other hand, is much more labile than that of the other pyrimidine nucleotides. The nucleoside-3′,5′ phosphates are decomposed more rapidly in alkali than the nucleoside-2′, -3′, -5′, or -2′,3′ cyclic phosphates, but the difference is not so marked as in the case of acid hydrolysis. Since cyclic phosphates in a six-membered ring are more stable than those in a five-membered ring, the increased instability of the nucleoside-3′,5′ phosphates must be due to the introduction of strain into the ring system due to the unfavourable *trans*-configuration of the two hydroxyl groups.

Adenosine-3′,5′ phosphate has been isolated as a factor stimulating the conversion of inactive glycogen phosphorylase to the active form in liver preparations (118), and guanosine-3′,5′ phosphate has been isolated from rat urine (119).

Nucleoside diphosphates are commonly encountered in both the enzymic and alkaline hydrolysates of RNA and DNA.

A mixture of pyrimidine ribonucleoside-2′,5′ and -3′,5′ diphosphates has been prepared by phosphorylating uridine and cytidine with a mixture of phosphoric acid and phosphorus pentoxide (122), and a corresponding mixture of adenosine diphosphates has been prepared from adenosine on treatment with excess dibenzyl phosphorochloridate (123). β-Cyanoethyl phosphate and dicyclohexyl carbodiimide have also been used to synthesize nucleoside diphosphates (109).

2.10 Biochemical function of mononucleotides

The main biochemical role of mononucleotides is to function as sources of the nucleoside pyro- and tri-phosphates. The nucleoside pyro- and tri-phosphates are phosphorylating agents and are the starting materials for the synthesis of nucleic acids and nucleotide coenzymes.

This aspect of the biochemistry of mononucleotides will be mentioned in Chapters 3 and 5 of this Monograph.

2.11 Biosynthesis of nucleosides and nucleotides

Purines are formed *in vivo* by the synthesis of first the imidazole ring then the pyrimidine ring. Using partially purified enzymes from pigeon liver, the steps in the enzymic synthesis of inosinic acid have been unravelled mainly by Buchanan and his co-workers (56).

Ribose-5 phosphate is pyrophosphorylated by ATP to give ribose-1 pyrophosphate-5 phosphate. This is one of the rare instances when ATP functions as a pyrophosphorylating agent rather than a phosphorylating agent.

$$(HO)_2POCH_2 \overset{OH}{\underset{HO\ OH}{\diamond}} + ATP \longrightarrow (HO)_2POCH_2 \overset{O}{\underset{HO\ OH\ OH\ \ \ OH}{\diamond}} O-P-O-P-OH + AMP$$

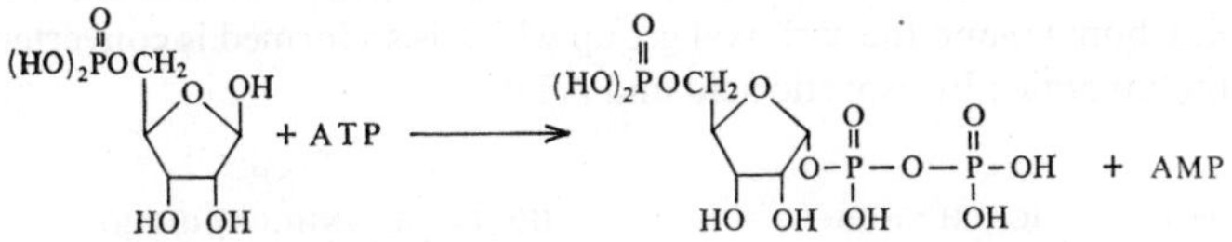

The ribose-1 pyrophosphate-5 phosphate then reacts with glutamine to give ribosylamine-5 phosphate.

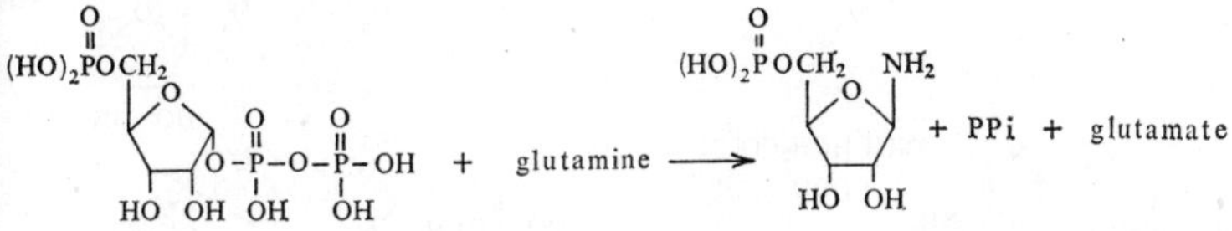

$$(HO)_2POCH_2 \overset{O\ \ \ O}{\underset{HO\ OH\ OH\ \ \ OH}{\diamond}} O-P-O-P-OH + \text{glutamine} \longrightarrow (HO)_2POCH_2 \overset{NH_2}{\underset{HO\ OH}{\diamond}} + PPi + \text{glutamate}$$

Ribosylamine-5 phosphate and glycine react in the presence of ATP to give the glycyl derivative. In this reaction the acylating species must be a mixed anhydride of ADP and glycine as the other products of the reaction are ADP and inorganic phosphate.

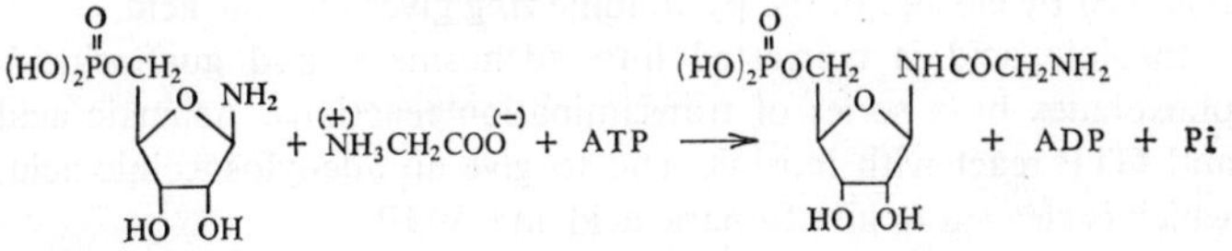

$$(HO)_2POCH_2 \overset{NH_2}{\underset{HO\ OH}{\diamond}} + \overset{(+)}{NH_3}CH_2COO^{(-)} + ATP \longrightarrow (HO)_2POCH_2 \overset{NHCOCH_2NH_2}{\underset{HO\ OH}{\diamond}} + ADP + Pi$$

The glycyl ribosylamine-5 phosphate is then formylated by anhydroformyl tetrahydrofolic acid.

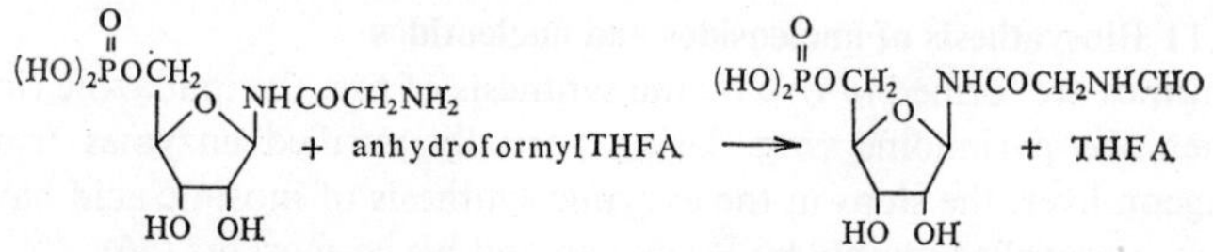

(HO)₂POCH₂
O
NHCOCH₂NH₂
HO OH
+ anhydroformylTHFA
(HO)₂POCH₂
NHCOCH₂NHCHO
+ THFA

The carbonyl group which originated from the glycine residue is then converted into an amidine group by the action of ATP and glutamine. The amidine is then cyclized by an enzyme, which requires ATP for a cofactor, to an amino imidazole ribotide. This amino imidazole ribotide is carboxylated by carbon dioxide (or bicarbonate) and the carboxyl group which is so formed is converted into an amide by aspartic acid and ATP.

(HO)₂POCH₂
NHCOCH₂NHCHO
HO OH
glutamine
NH
NHCCH₂NHCHO
NH₂
COOH
CO₂
CONHCHCH₂COOH
COOH
ATP
aspartic acid

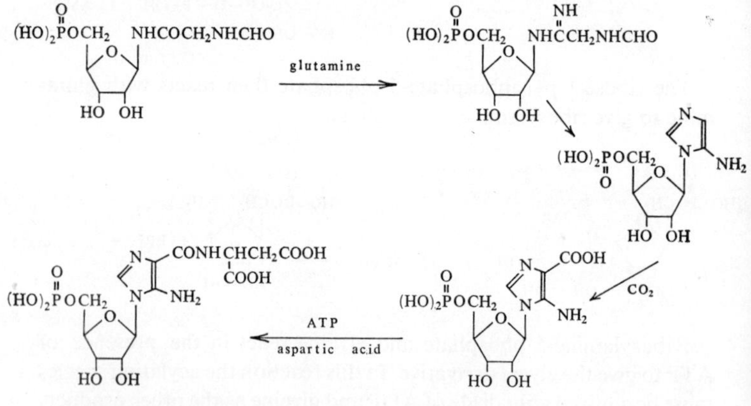

Cleavage of this amide gives fumaric acid and 5-amino 1-β-D-ribofuranosyl imidazole-4 carboxamide-5′ phosphate. Formylation followed by closure of the pyrimidine ring gives inosinic acid.

Inosinic acid is converted into adenosine-5′ and guanosine-5 phosphates by a series of transamination reactions. Aspartic acid and GTP react with inosinic acid to give an adenylosuccinic acid, which is cleaved to give fumaric acid and AMP.

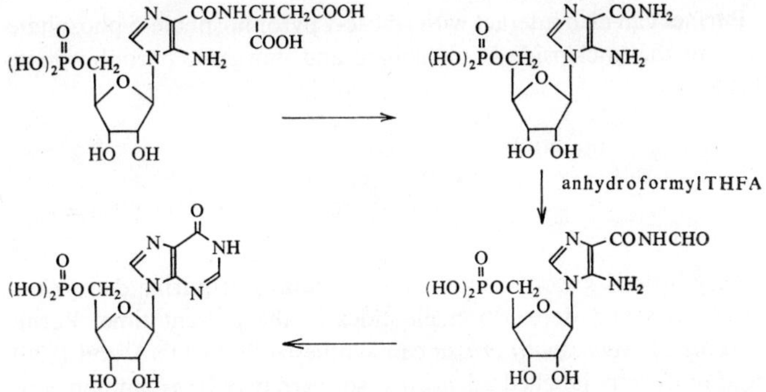

Oxidation of inosinic acid by a dehydrogenase which requires NAD^+ as a cofactor gives xanthosine-5′ phosphate. This is then aminated by glutamine to guanosine-5′ phosphate.

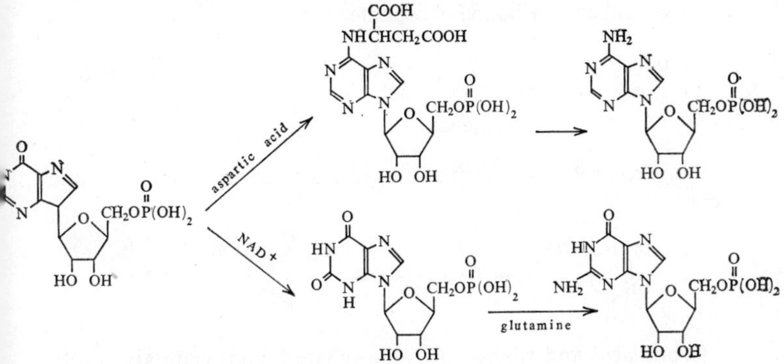

Preformed purines can act as precursors in the biosynthesis of nucleosides and nucleotides. Purines in the presence of a nucleoside phosphorylase can react with ribose-1 phosphate to give the nucleoside and inorganic phosphate (124).

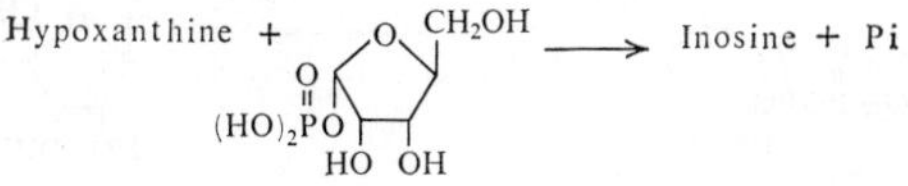

Purines can also interact with ribose-1 pyrophosphate-5 phosphate to form the nucleoside-5′ phosphate and inorganic pyrophosphate (125).

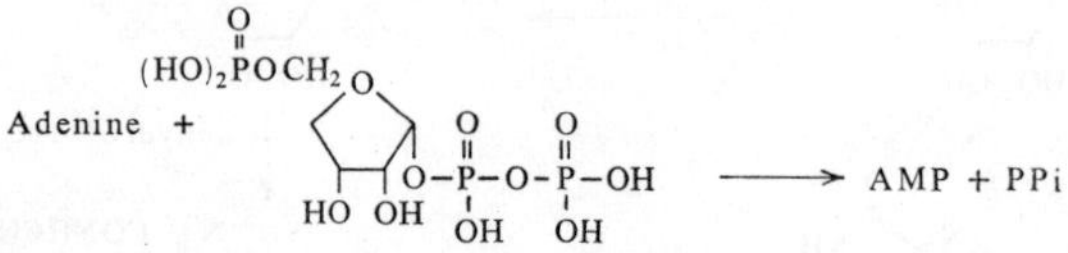

Adenine + [ribose-1 pyrophosphate-5 phosphate structure] ⟶ AMP + PPi

Very little is known about the biosynthesis of purine deoxyribonucleosides and deoxyribonucleotides at the present time. Purine mutants of *Neurospora crassa* can synthesize both DNA and RNA from uniformly labelled adenosine, so there may be a common early stage in the biosynthesis of the ribo- and deoxyribo- series.

A key intermediate in the biosynthesis of pyrimidine nucleosides and nucleotides is orotic acid, uracil-4 carboxylic acid. Dihydroorotic acid is formed by the cyclization of the reaction product of aspartic acid and carbamyl phosphate (126).

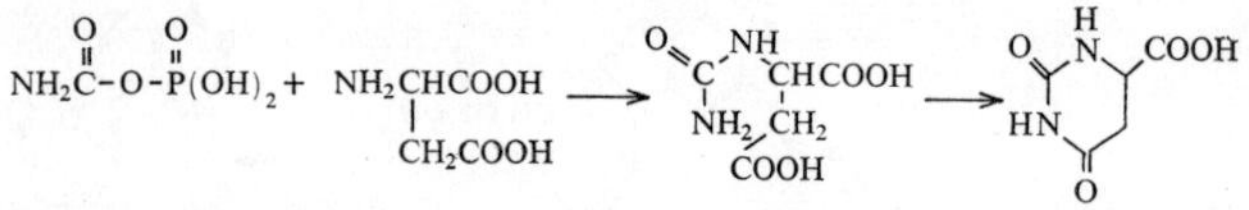

$$NH_2C-O-P(OH)_2 + NH_2CHCOOH \longrightarrow \cdots \longrightarrow \cdots$$

Dihydro-orotic acid is then dehydrogenated by FAD to orotic acid.

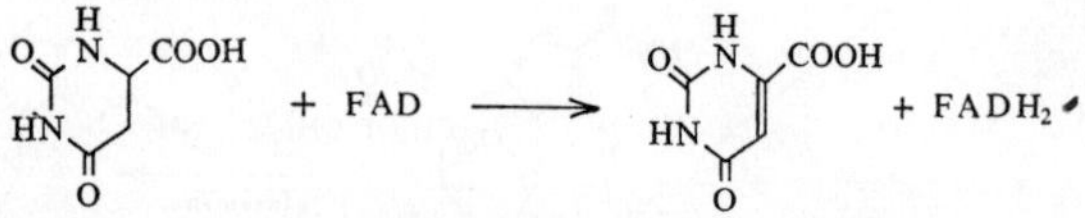

+ FAD ⟶ + FADH₂

Orotic acid and ribose-1 pyrophosphate-5 phosphate give orotidine-4′ phosphate (4-carboxy UMP) which is decarboxylated to UMP.

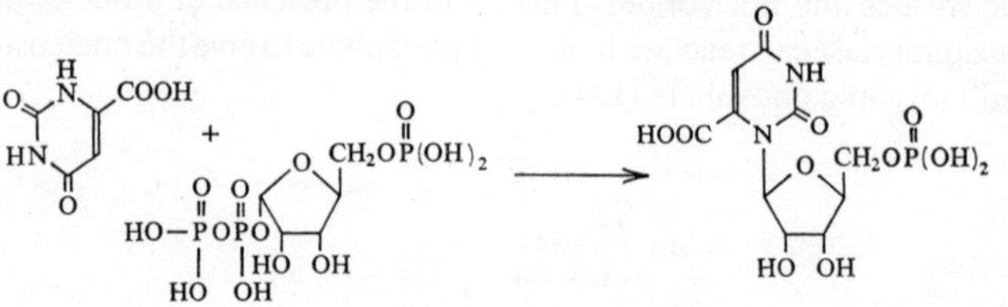

UMP is then phosphorylated by two molecules of ATP to UTP which is then aminated by either ammonia or glutamine to CTP

$$UTP + NH_3 + ATP \longrightarrow CTP + ADP + P_i$$

In addition to the pathway involving orotic acid, it appears that pyrimidines can react with ribose-1 pyrophosphate-5 phosphate to give the corresponding nucleotides (127). This reaction is analogous to that for purine nucleotides which has been mentioned above.

Relatively little is known about the biosynthesis of pyrimidine deoxynucleosides and deoxynucleotides. Thymidine-5' phosphate is formed *in vivo* by the methylation of deoxyuridine-5' phosphate with methylene tetrahydrofolate (128).

$$dUMP + methylene\ THFA \longrightarrow dTMP$$

The methylene group is probably transferred as a hydroxymethyl group which is then dehydrated and reduced to a methyl group.

Deoxyuridine-5' phosphate may be formed from uridine-5' phosphate by some reductive process. However, extracts of *Escherichia Coli* catalyze the formation of deoxycytidine nucleotides from CMP (129). The reduction of CDP to dCDP, which is the main reductive reaction, appears to require NADH as a cofactor.

REFERENCES

1. KAY, SIMMONS, and DOUNCE, (1952), *JACS*, **74**, 1724.
2. DOUNCE and KAY (1953), *JACS*, **75**, 4041.
3. BRADLEY and RICH (1956), *JACS*, **78**, 5898.
4. MIURA and SUZUKI (1956), *BBA*, **22**, 565.
5. KIRBY (1962), *BBA*, **61**, 506.
6. PORATH and FLODIN (1959), *Nature*, **183**, 1657.
7. BOMAN and HJERTEN (1962), *Arch. Biochem. Biophys.*, Suppl. 1., 276.
8. LEVENE and DMOCHOWSKI (1931), *JBC*, **93**, 563.
9. LEVENE and HARRIS (1933), *JBC*, **101**, 419.
10. LEVENE and JACOBS (1910), *Ber.*, **43**, 3150.
11. LORING, BORTNER, LEVY, and HAMMELL (1952) *JBC*, **196**, 807
12. HURST (1956), *Canad. J. Biochem. Physiol.*, **34**, 265.

13. VOLKIN, KHYM, and COHN (1951), *JACS*, **73**, 1533.
14. CARTER (1951), *JACS*, **73**, 1537.
15. MARKHAM and SMITH (1952), *BJ*, **52**, 558.
16. RUSHIZKY and SOBER (1962), *JBC*, **237**, 2883.
17. COHN and VOLKIN (1953), *JBC*, **203**, 319.
18. COHN (1955), *The Nucleic Acids*, Vol. I, eds. Chargaff and Davidson, Academic Press, N.Y., p. 211.
19. NILSSON and SJUNNESSON (1961), *Acta Chem. Scand.*, **15**, 1017.
20. LEVENE and JACOBS (1909), *Ber.*, **42**, 1198.
21. LEVENE and JACOBS (1911), *Ber.*, **44**, 746.
22. VAN EKENSTEIN and BLANKSMA (1913), *Chem. Weekblad*, **10**, 664.
23. KARRER, BECKER, BENZ, FREI, SALOMON, and SCHÖPP (1935), *Helv. Chim. Acta*, **18**, 1435.
24. LEVENE and LONDON (1929), *JBC*, **81**, 711.
25. LEVENE, MIKESKA, and MORI (1930), *JBC*, **85**, 785.
26. OVEREND and LALAND (1954), *Acta Chem. Scand.*, **8**, 192.
27. OVEREND and STACEY (1953), *Adv. Carbohydrate Chem.*, **8**, 45.
28. OHTA and MAKINO (1951), *Science*, **113**, 273.
29. SOWDEN (1957), *Biochem. Preps.*, **5**, 75.
30. DIEHL and FLETCHER (1961), *Biochem. Preps.*, **8**, 49.
31. FURBERG (1960), *Acta Chem. Scand.*, **14**, 1357.
32. BARKER and SHAW (1959), *JCS*, 584.
33. CHARGAFF, VISCHER, DONIGER, GREEN, and MISANI (1949), *JBC*, **177**, 405.
34. WYATT (1951), *BJ*, **48**, 584.
35. DUNN (1960), *BBA*, **38**, 176.
36. MARSHAK (1951), *PNAS*, **37**, 299.
37. LEHMAN and PRATT (1960), *JBC*, **235**, 3254.
38. LEVENE and BASS (1931), *Nucleic Acids*, A. C. S. Monograph No. 56, Reinhold, N.Y., p. 35.
39. DAVIDSON and BAUDISCH (1926), *JACS*, **48**, 2379.
40. LYTHGOE (1949), *Quart. Rev.*, **3**, 181.
41. KENNER and TODD (1957), *Heterocyclic Compounds*, Vol. VI, ed. by Elderfield, Wiley, N.Y., p. 234.
42. WATSON and CRICK (1953), *Nature*, **171**, 964.
43. MARSHALL and WALKER (1951), *JCS*, 1004.
44. BROWN, HOERGER, and MASON (1955), *JCS*, 4035.
45. KENNER, REESE, and TODD (1955), *JCS*, 855.
46. PAULING and COREY (1956), *Arch. Biochim. Biophys.*, **65**, 164.
47. GERDIL (1961), *Acta Cryst.*, **14**, 333.
48. FURBERG (1950), *Acta Chem. Scand.*, **4**, 751.

49. PARRY (1954), *Acta Cryst*, **7**, 313.
50. LITTLEFIELD and DUNN (1958), *BJ*, **70**, 642.
51. SMITH and DUNN (1959), *BJ*, **72**, 294.
52. LEVENE and BASS (1931), *Nucleic Acids*, A.C.S., Monograph No. 56, Reinhold, N.Y., p. 95.
53. FISCHER and ACH (1895), *Ber.*, **28**, 2473.
54. TRAUBE (1900), *Ber.*, **33**, 1371.
55. LISTER (1961), *Rev. Pure and App. Chem.*, **11**, 178.
56. BUCHANAN (1961), *The Nucleic Acids*, Vol. III, eds. Chargaff and Davidson, Academic Press, N.Y., p. 303.
57. TAYLOR, OSDENE, RICHTER, and VOGL (1957), *CIBA Symposium on the Chemistry and Biology of Purines*, Churchill, London, p. 20.
58. ORO and KIMBALL (1962), *Arch. Biochim. Biophys.*, **96**, 293.
59. MASON (1957), *CIBA Symposium on the Chemistry and Biology of Purines*, Churchill, London, p. 60.
60. MASON (1954), *JCS*, 2071.
61. ANGELL (1961), *JCS*, 504.
62. SCHULTZE and BOSSHARD (1885), *Z. Physiol. Chem.*, **9**, 420.
63. LEVENE and JACOBS (1909), *Ber.*, **42**, 2469, 2703.
64. LEVENE and LA FORGE (1912), *Ber.*, **45**, 608.
65. BURKE (1955), *J. Org. Chem.*, **20**, 643.
66. LEVENE (1925), *JBC*, **63**, 653.
67. LEVENE and TIPSON (1934), *JBC*, **104**, 385.
68. FOX and WEMPEN (1959), *Adv. Carbohydrate Chem.*, **14**, 283.
69. BROWN, PARIHAR, REESE, and TODD (1958), *JCS*, 3035.
70. LEVENE and TIPSON (1935), *JBC*, **111**, 313.
71. GULLAND and HOLIDAY (1936), *JCS*, 765.
72. GULLAND and STOREY (1938), *JCS*, 259, 692.
73. KENNER, TAYLOR, and TODD (1949), *JCS*, 1620.
74. LEVENE and TIPSON (1933), *JBC*, **101**, 529.
75. LYTHGOE and TODD (1944), *JCS*, 592.
76. BROWN and LYTHGOE (1950), *JCS*, 1990.
77. JARDETSKY (1962), *JACS*, **84**, 62.
78. DAVOLL, LYTHGOE, and TODD (1946), *JCS*, 833.
79. CLARK, TODD, and ZUSSMAN (1951), *JCS*, 2952.
80. FISCHER and HELFERICH (1914), *Ber.*, **47**, 210.
81. ULBRICHT (1962), *Angew. Chem. (Internat. Edn.)*, **1**, 476.
82. BAKER (1957), *CIBA Symposium on the Chemistry and Biology of Purines*, Churchill, London, p. 120.
83. NESS and FLETCHER (1960), *JACS*, **82**, 3434.
84. VENNER (1960), *Ber.*, **93**, 140.

85. FOX, YUNG, WEMPEN, and HOFFER (1961), *JACS*, **83**, 4066.
86. HOFFER (1960), *Ber.*, **93**, 2777.
87. COHN (1959), *BBA*, **32**, 569.
88. COHN (1960), *JBC*, **235**, 1488.
89. COHN and MICHELSON (1962), *Biochem.*, **1**, 490.
90. SHAPIRO and CHAMBERS (1961), *JACS*, **83**, 3920.
91. HEINRIKSON and GOLDWASSER (1963), *JBC*, **238**, PC 485.
92. LIS and LIS (1962), *BBA*, **61**, 799.
93. LIEBIG (1847), *Annalen*, **62**, 317.
94. LEVENE and BASS (1931), *Nucleic Acids*, A.C.S., Monograph No. 56, Reinhold, N.Y., p. 186.
95. BROWN and TODD (1952), *JCS*, 44.
96. CARTER and COHN (1949), *Fed. Proc.*, **8**, 190.
97. BROWN, HAYNES, and TODD (1950), *JCS*, 3299.
98. KHYM, DOHERTY, VOLKIN, and COHN (1953), *JACS*, **75**, 1262.
99. LEVENE and STILLER (1934), *JBC*, **104**, 299.
100. LEVENE and TIPSON (1937), *JBC*, **121**, 131.
101. BADDILEY and TODD (1947), *JCS*, 648.
102. MICHELSON and TODD (1949), *JCS*, 2476.
103. HALL and KHORANA (1954), *JACS*, **76**, 5056.
104. WEIMANN and KHORANA (1962), *JACS*, **84**, 4329.
105. CREMLYN, KENNER, and TODD (1960), *JCS*, 4511.
106. CRAMER and WINTER (1959), *Ber.*, **92**, 2761.
107. KENNER, REESE, and TODD (1958), *JCS*, 546.
108. CRAMER and WEIMANN (1961), *Ber.*, **94**, 996.
109. TENER (1961), *JACS*, **83**, 159.
110. BROWN, MAGRATH, and TODD (1952), *JCS*, 2708.
111. MICHELSON, SZABO, and TODD (1956), *JCS*, 1546.
112. SMRT and SORM (1962), *Coll. Czech. Chem. Commun.*, **27**, 75.
113. BROWN and TODD (1952), *JCS*, 52.
114. KUMAMOTO, COX, and WESTHEIMER (1956), *JACS*, **78**, 4858.
115. KHORANA, TENER, WRIGHT, AND MOFFATT (1957), *JACS*, **79**, 430.
116. COX, WALL, and WESTHEIMER (1959), *Chem. and Ind.*, 929.
117. DEKKER and KHORANA (1954), *JACS*, **76**, 3522.
118. SUTHERLAND and RALL (1958), *JBC*, **232**, 1065, 1077.
119. ASHMAN, LIPTON, MELICOW, and PRICE (1963), *Biochem. Biophys. Res. Commun.*, **11**, 330.
120. COOK, LIPKIN, and MARKHAM (1959), *JACS*, **81**, 6198.
121. SMITH, DRUMMOND, and KHORANA (1961), *JACS*, **83**, 698.
122. HALL and KHORANA (1955), *JACS*, **77**, 1871.
123. MOFFATT and KHORANA (1961), *JACS*, **83**, 663.

124. KALCKAR (1947), *Symp. Soc. Exp. Biol.*, **1**, 38.
125. BUCHANAN, FLAKS, HARTMAN, LEVENBERG, LUKENS, AND WARREN (1957), *CIBA Foundation Symposium on the Chemistry and Biology of Purines*, Churchill, London, p, 233.
126. CROSBIE (1960), *The Nucleic Acids*, Vol. III, eds. Chargaff and Davidson, Academic Press, N.Y., p. 323.
127. REICHARD (1959), *Adv. in Enzymol.*, **21**, 263.
128. BLAKELY (1963), *JBC*, **238**, 2113.
129. REICHARD (1963), *JBC*, **238**, 3513.

CHAPTER THREE

Nucleotide Coenzymes

3.1 Introduction

Nucleotide coenzymes can catalyse a wide variety of biochemical reactions including oxidation-reduction processes and the synthesis of such macromolecules as nucleic acids, polysaccharides, and glycerides. The main reactions of the nucleotide coenzymes to be described in this chapter are outlined in the following table.

Coenzyme	*Biochemical function*
Nucleoside di- and triphosphates	Phosphorylation reactions
	Coenzyme synthesis
	Nucleic acid synthesis
Nicotinamide-adenine dinucleotide	Oxidation-reduction
Nicotinamide-adenine dinucleotide phosphate	Oxidation-reduction
Flavin mononucleotide	Oxidation-reduction
Flavin-adenine dinucleotide	Oxidation-reduction
Coenzyme A	Acyl transfer
	Fatty acid synthesis
	Glyceride synthesis
Nucleoside diphosphate sugars	Polysaccharide synthesis
	Phospholipid synthesis
	Teichoic acid synthesis

The nucleotide coenzymes will be described in the order shown in the above table, starting with the 'simple' nucleoside-5′ polyphosphates (ADP, ATP, etc.). The oxidation-reduction coenzymes will be described next; these compounds are biochemically active by virtue of oxidation-reduction processes which take place in the non-nucleotidic portion of the molecule. Finally the group transfer coenzymes will be described.

3.2 Nucleoside-5′ polyphosphates

Introduction. The nucleoside-5′ polyphosphates which are most widespread in nature are adenosine diphosphate (ADP) (I) and adenosine triphosphate (ATP) (II).

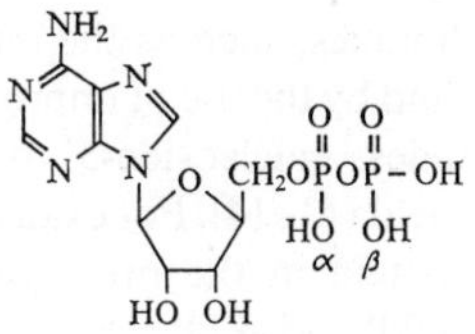

(I) 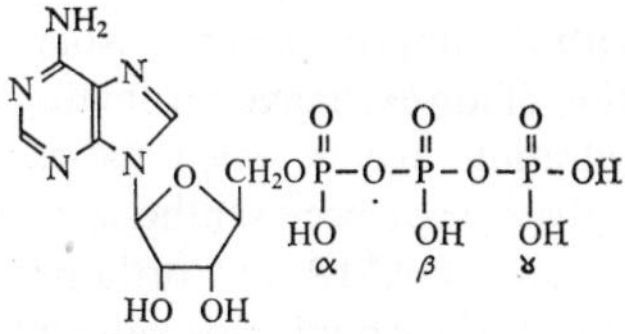   (II)

These two compounds are involved in transphosphorylation reactions and ATP can phosphorylate a substrate (S) with the production of ADP and the phosphorylated substrate.

$$ATP + S \rightleftharpoons ADP + S—H_2PO_4$$

These reactions are formally reversible, and ADP can be phosphorylated enzymically by a reactive phosphate.

Discovery. ADP and ATP were first discovered in muscle by Fiske and Subbarow (1). The correct structural formulae of the two co-enzymes were deduced by Lohmann when he found that ADP had two primary and one secondary acid dissociations, while ATP had three primary and one secondary acid dissociations (2). Proof of the position of attachment of the polyphosphate residue to the nucleoside was provided by Lythgoe and Todd, who showed that ATP consumed one equivalent of metaperiodate and hence the triphosphate residue must be attached to the 5′ hydroxyl group (3).

The di- and triphosphates of guanosine, uridine, cytidine, and thymidine have all been isolated from natural sources (4, 5, 6) (see section 6 of this chapter). Deoxynucleoside triphosphates have been prepared enzymically by the incubation of the corresponding mono-phosphate with an enzyme from *Escherichia Coli* (7), and deoxy-nucleoside diphosphates have been isolated after the hydrolysis of deoxynucleoside diphosphate sugars (8, 9).

Final confirmation of the structure of nucleoside-5′ polyphosphates was provided by their synthesis. ADP and ATP were first synthesized by the phosphorochloridate method (10, 11), the yields of ADP and ATP obtained by this method were low owing to the instability of pyro- and triphosphate intermediates in the reaction.

With the improvement of isolation techniques, such as the intro-duction of ion exchange chromatography, and by the use of improved dehydrating agents, such as carbodiimides, nucleoside-5′ poly-phosphates have been synthesized in high yield (12–14). For example, a mixture of AMP and orthophosphoric acid in the presence of dicyclohexyl carbodiimide will give both ADP and ATP (15).

As a mixture of products is generally obtained during the synthesis of unsymmetrical pyrophosphates with carbodiimides, a more specific method of pyrophosphate synthesis has been developed involving phosphoramidates. Monoesterified phosphoramidates are good phosphorylating agents, and have been used in the synthesis of ADP and ATP (16), and as phosphoramidates do not phosphorylate alcohols under normal conditions, protecting groups are unnecessary for alcoholic hydroxyl groups. Nucleotide-5′ phosphoramidates have been prepared from nucleotide-5′ phosphates and an amine in the presence of dicyclohexyl carbodiimide (17), and have been used in the synthesis of such nucleotide coenzymes as ATP, FAD, and CoA.

The relative positions of the polyphosphate group and the adenine moiety of ADP and ATP have been deduced by physical methods.

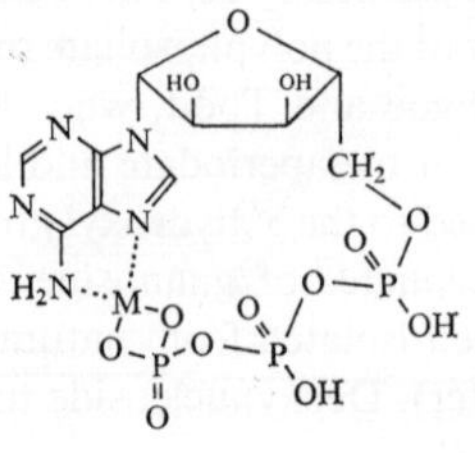

For example, nuclear magnetic resonance spectroscopy (18) indicates that the polyphosphate chain and the adenine moiety can form complexes with transition metal ions.

Both adenosine-5' tetra- and penta-phosphates have been isolated from commercial samples of ATP which have been prepared from ox muscle (19, 20). Adenosine-5' tetra-phosphate is inactive in phosphate transfer reactions and it is not known whether these polyphosphates are artefacts or whether they have a biochemical function which is still unknown (21).

Biosynthesis. Adenosine triphosphate is produced as the end product of three main metabolic processes, viz.; substrate level oxidative phosphorylation, respiratory chain oxidative phosphorylation, and photosynthetic phosphorylation (22). In every case the final stage in the synthesis of ATP is the phosphorylation of ADP by an 'energy rich' phosphorylating agent such as phospho-enol pyruvate or acetyl phosphate.

$$ADP + CH_3COOPO_3H_2 \rightleftharpoons ATP + CH_3COOH$$

ADP can be formed enzymically by the phosphorylation of AMP by ATP, this reaction is catalysed by myokinase and is reversible.

$$AMP + ATP \rightleftharpoons 2 ADP$$

Biochemical properties. The α and the γ phosphorus atoms of ATP are more susceptible towards attack by nucleophiles than the β phosphorus atom (23). Thus a nucleophilic substrate (S) can attack the terminal (γ) phosphorus atom of ATP giving the phosphorylated nucleophile and ADP.

(i) $$ATP + S \rightleftharpoons SH_2PO_4 + ADP$$

This is a very common enzymic route to phosphomonoesters, for example sugar phosphates, and is of importance in the biosynthesis of other nucleoside triphosphates. Enzymes which catalyse this type of reaction are called 'kinases'.

A nucleophilic substrate, usually a phosphate, (S) can also attack the α phosphorus atom of ATP to produce an adenosine-5' pyrophosphate ester and inorganic pyrophosphate. This is the route to most nucleotide coenzymes which are diesters of pyrophosphoric acid (FAD, NAD, CoA).

(ii) $ATP + FMN \rightleftharpoons FAD + PP_i$

Other nucleoside triphosphates (UTP, CTP, GTP) can react in this fashion and most nucleoside diphosphate sugars are synthesized by this reaction.

The enzymic synthesis of polynucleotides from nucleoside di- and triphosphates is an example of reaction (i). An enzyme, DNA polymerase, will incorporate deoxynucleoside triphosphates into a primer polydeoxynucleotide with the release of inorganic pyrophosphate (7). Similar polymerases have been isolated which will incorporate nucleoside-5' triphosphates into RNA (24). Nucleoside-5' diphosphates are polymerized by polynucleotide phosphorylase with the concomitant liberation of orthophosphate (25). The biosynthesis of polynucleotides by these three classes of enzyme is discussed in detail in Chapter 5.

The β phosphorus atom of ATP is much less susceptible towards nucleophilic attack than the α and γ atoms and only two pyrophosphokinases have been observed at the present time. One catalyses the conversion of thamine to thiamine pyrophosphate, a reaction which is discussed in Chapter 4. The other catalyses the synthesis of ribose-1 pyrophosphate-5 phosphate from ribose 5-phosphate (26),

ribose 5-phosphate + ATP $\rightleftharpoons$ ribose-1 pyrophosphate-5 phosphate
$+ AMP$

Guanosine triphosphate is required during the RNA directed biosynthesis of protein (27). The requirement of the enzyme systems for GTP is very specific and only ITP, of the other nucleoside triphosphates, shows any activity when it replaces GTP (28). The role of GTP in protein biosynthesis is, however, unknown as the high guanosine triphosphatase activity of the cell free preparations, which have been used so far, makes the study of the fate of the GTP impracticable.

3.3 The pyridine coenzymes

Discovery and structural determination. Nicotinamide-adenine dinucleotide (NAD⁺) (III), the heat stable cofactor of alcoholic fermentation, was discovered by Harden and Young in 1906 (29), and hence was the first nucleotide coenzyme to be discovered. However, NAD⁺ was not isolated until 1936, when both von Euler (30), and Warburg and Christian (31) obtained the coenzyme in a purified form.

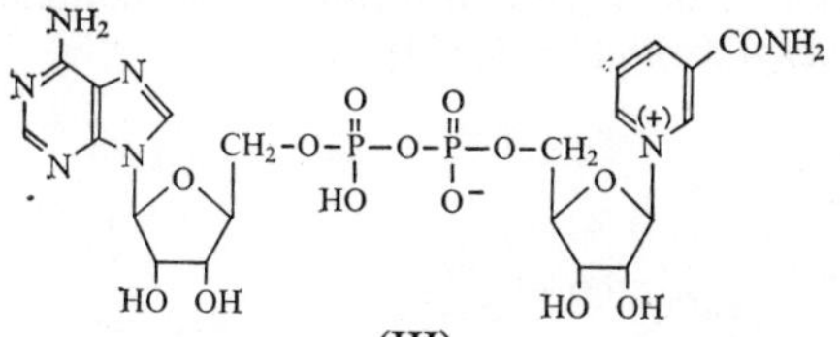

(III)

The heat stable coenzyme of D-glucose-6 phosphate dehydrogenase, with very similar properties to those of NAD⁺, had been isolated in 1931 by Warburg and Christian from yeast (32). This coenzyme is now known as nicotinamide-adenine dinucleotide phosphate (NADP⁺) (IV), and like NAD⁺ it is the cofactor of a number of dehydrogenases.

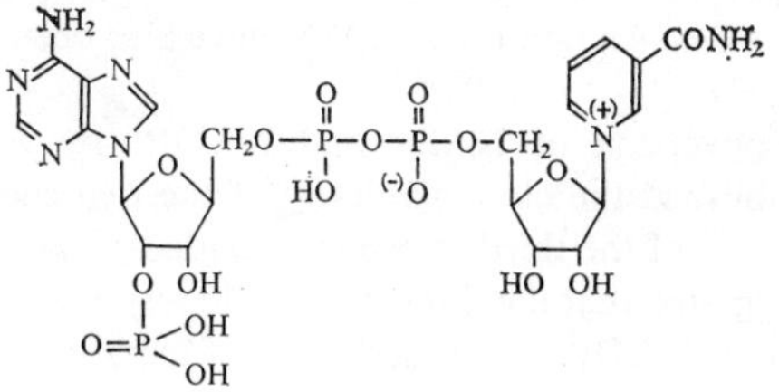

(IV)

Hydrolysis of NAD⁺ with acid liberates adenine and nicotinamide (30) together with two equivalents of ribose-5 phosphate per molecule (33). Both adenosine mono- and di-phosphates can be isolated from

4

the alkaline hydrolysates of the coenzyme (34). From the reversible oxidation and reduction of NAD$^+$, Karrer suggested that the nitrogen atom of the pyridine ring in the nicotinamide portion might be quaternary, and that one of the ribosyl moieties might be joined to this nitrogen atom (35). NAD$^+$ is cleaved into AMP and the 5' phosphate of N-ribosyl nicotinamide (nicotinamide mononucleotide) (V) by a pyrophosphatase, which confirms the hypothesis that the molecule is a P^1, P^2-diester of pyrophosphoric acid (36).

Synthesis. Nicotinamide-adenine dinucleotide was synthesized by treating a mixture of AMP and nicotinamide mononucleotide (V) with dicyclohexyl carbodiimide (37).

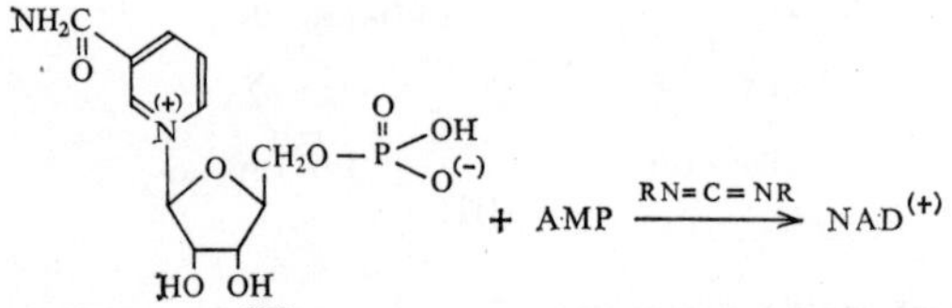

(V)

Phosphorylation of nicotinamide mononucleoside with phosphorus oxychloride is a convenient synthetic method for the preparation of nicotinamide mononucleotide. Nicotinamide mononucleoside can be prepared from tri-acetyl ribofuranosyl chloride and nicotinamide (38), an adaptation of one of the techniques for the preparation of purine nucleosides. Analogues of NAD$^+$ have also been prepared by this method (39).

The interconversion of NAD$^+$ and NADP$^+$ by yeast extracts (40, 41), established the close similarity of the two coenzymes and only the position of the third phosphate residue remained in doubt. von Euler suggested that the three phosphate residues were linked in a chain and that NADP$^+$ was a derivative of tripolyphosphoric acid (42). Schlenk, on the other hand, proposed that the third phosphate was attached to a hydroxyl of the adenosine moiety (43). Kornberg finally settled the position of the third phosphate residue when he isolated adenosine-2',5' diphosphate from the reaction between NADP$^+$ and a nucleotide pyrophosphatase (44).

Biosynthesis. The biosynthesis of NAD^+ is thought to involve the preliminary formation of a nicotinic acid-adenine dinucleotide and the subsequent conversion of the carboxylic acid group of this compound to an amide function (45). The proposed pathway is as follows.

Nicotinic acid + ribose 5-phosphate 1-pyrophosphate $\rightleftharpoons$
nicotinic acid mononucleotide + PP_i

Nicotinic acid mononucleotide + ATP $\rightleftharpoons$
nicotinic acid-adenine dinucleotide

Nicotinic acid-adenine dinucleotide + glutamine + ATP $\rightleftharpoons$
$NAD^+ + AMP + PP_i$

$NADP^+$ is synthesized by the phosphorylation of NAD^+ by ATP (40, 41).

$$NAD^+ + ATP \rightleftharpoons NADP^+ + ADP$$

Position of hydrogen transfer. The mechanism of hydrogen transfer by the nicotinamide coenzymes has been the subject of much speculation and study ever since the coenzymes were discovered. As has been mentioned above, Karrer suggested that the pyridine ring was involved in the hydrogen transfer process (35) but did not establish the actual site of reduction in the ring.

Westheimer and co-workers observed that direct transfer of deuterium to NAD^+ occurred when 1,1-dideutero ethanol was dehydrogenated by NAD^+ and yeast alcohol dehydrogenase (46).

$$CH_3CD_2OH + NAD^+ \rightleftharpoons \text{deuterated-NAD} + CH_3CDO$$

If enzymically deuterated NAD were reoxidized enzymically, all the deuterium in the NAD was lost. However, if chemically deuterated NAD (prepared by the reduction of NAD^+ with hydrosulphite in deuterium oxide) were oxidized enzymically, only about half of the deuterium was lost (47).

The site of the hydrogen transfer in the pyridine was established as para to the nitrogen atom in the following way. Chemically deuterated NAD^+ was oxidized enzymically and then cleaved by means of a nicotinamide adenine dinucleotidase to deuterated nicotinamide. This was oxidized with alkaline ferricyanide with no loss of deuterium. As alkaline ferricyanide will oxidise N-methyl nicotinamide to a mixture of the 2- and 6- pyridones (48), neither the 2 nor the 6 position were involved in the reduction of NAD^+ (49).

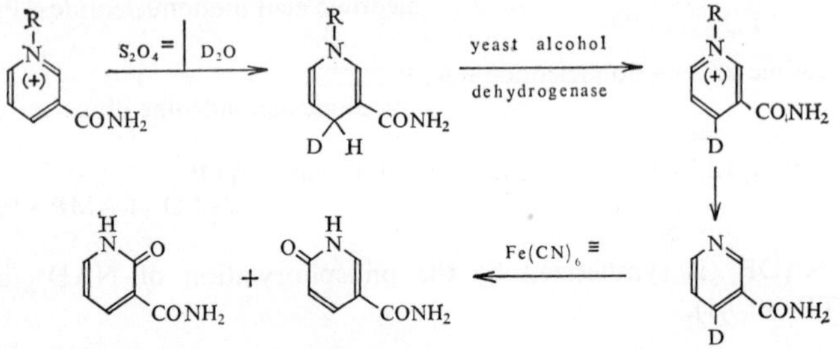

Further evidence that the reduction of NAD^+ takes place in the para position was provided by Westheimer, who showed that only N-benzyl 4-deutero nicotinamide and neither the 2- nor the 6-deuterated N-benzyl nicotinamides transferred deuterium to a model hydrogen acceptor (50).

Nuclear magnetic resonance spectra of dihydro N-methyl nicotinamide and its deuterated analogue confirm that reduction takes place in the 4-position (51, 52). Thus, reduced nicotinamide-adenine dinucleotide (NADH) may be formulated as (VI).

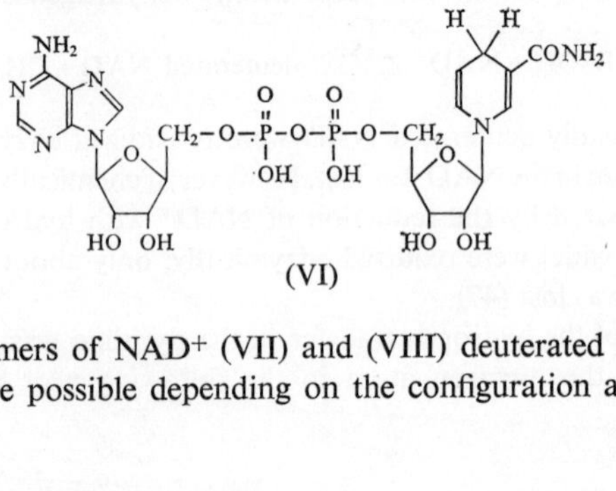

(VI)

Two isomers of NAD^+ (VII) and (VIII) deuterated in the para position are possible depending on the configuration at C_4 in the pyridine ring. The enzymic reduction (deuteration) of NAD^+ must be stereospecific and only one of the isomers can be formed. This isomer must then be destroyed stereospecifically during the enzymic oxidation.

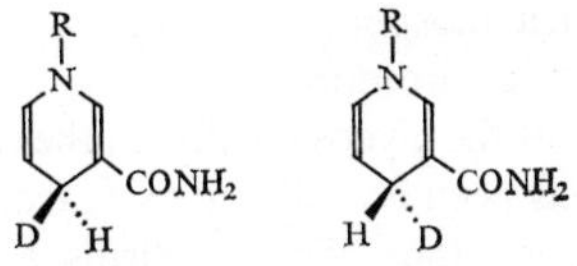

(VII)   (VIII)

The chemical reduction is not stereospecific and so both isomers are formed; one is consumed on oxidation of the mixture by the enzyme, leaving the other untouched.

Two classes of enzyme require NAD^+ as a cofactor, and the difference between these two classes depends on the difference in the direction of attack on the pyridine ring by the hydride ions during the reduction step. In one class, the hydride ion attacks from the 'top' of the ring, and in the other the hydride ion attacks from the 'underside' of the ring (53). The absolute configuration of deuterated NAD^+ for one of these classes of enzyme has been established in the following manner (54). The 3, 4, 5, and 6 carbon atoms of the pyridine ring of enzymically deuterated NAD^+ were converted into a deuterated succinic acid of known stereochemistry by the oxidative cleavage of the addition product of methanol and deuterated NAD^+.

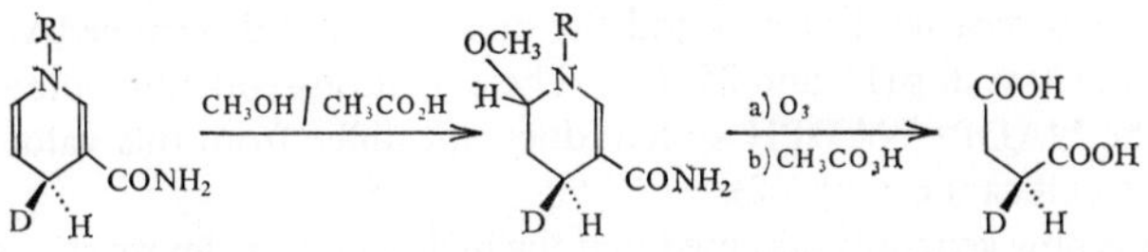

Spectra of NAD^+ and NADH. The ultraviolet absorption spectra of NAD^+ and NADH have been used both qualitatively and quantitatively in the study of reactions which are catalysed by the pyridine coenzymes. NAD^+ has a strong absorption band at 259 mμ due to both the adenine and the nicotinamide moieties; NADH on the other hand has a weaker band at 259 mμ, due solely to the adenine, and a second adsorption band at 338 mμ due to the dihydronicotinamide moiety (55). The ultraviolet spectra of NADP$^+$ and NADPH are sensibly the same as those of NAD$^+$ and NADH. This is not unexpected as the extra phosphate group on $C_{2'}$ of the adenosine does have much effect on the chromophore.

The configuration of the glycosidic link in the ribosyl nicotinamide portion of NAD$^+$ has been established as β, from nuclear magnetic resonance spectroscopy (56). This confirms an earlier deduction which was made from results obtained from the fluorescence spectrum of NADH (57).

Both the ultraviolet and the fluorescence spectra of NADH change when the reduced coenzyme is added to certain apoenzyme proteins. For example, when NADH is added to liver alcohol dehydrogenase there is a hypsochromic shift of the fluorescence maximum and an increase in intensity of fluorescence (58), which may be due to the formation of a complex between the NADH and a metal such as zinc. Yeast alcohol dehydrogenase, which is known to require zinc for its enzymic activity (59), causes an analogous shift in the fluorescence spectrum of NADH (60).

Mechanism of hydrogen transfer in the pyridine coenzymes. The oxidation-reduction potential of the system:

$$NAD^+ + H^- \rightleftharpoons NADH$$

has been measured *in vivo* and the most recently determined value is -0.320 v. at pH 7 and $25°$ (61). The oxidation-reduction potential of the NADP$^+$/NADPH system does not differ from this value by any significant extent (62).

It is now generally accepted that the hydrogen transfer reactions of the pyridine coenzymes are ionic rather than free radical processes, the reaction between NAD$^+$ and cyanide ions showing a strong resemblance to the reduction of NAD$^+$ by hydride ions. The addition product of NAD$^+$ and a cyanide ion is the 4-cyano compound (63), and this 4-cyano NAD will transfer cyanide to acceptors such as malachite green.

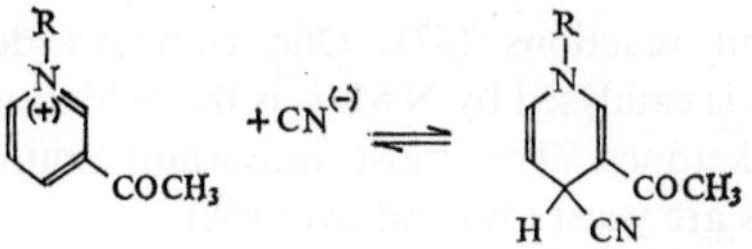

An analogue of NAD^+, 3-acetyl pyridine-adenine dinucleotide ($ANAD^+$) (XIX) is active in enzymic systems and will react with ethanol in the presence of yeast alcohol dehydrogenase. From the ratio of the equilibrium constant for the reaction between NAD^+ and ethanol to the equilibrium constant for the reaction between $ANAD^+$ and ethanol, a redox potential of -0.257 v for $ANAD^+$ is obtained. The ratio of the equilibrium constants for the reaction of both these compounds with cyanide ions has also been measured and this gives a value of -0.255 v for the redox potential of $ANAD^+$. This remarkable agreement suggests that the mechanism of the enzymically catalysed reaction between the pyridine coenzymes and hydrogen is the same as the mechanism of the reaction between the pyridine nucleotides and cyanide ions (64).

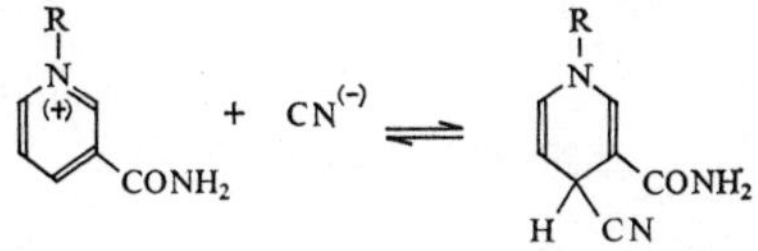

(XIX)

When NAD^+ was reduced in the presence of hydrogen radicals, products were obtained which were 6,6'-dipyridyls and these dimeric products were unable to transfer hydrogen atoms to acceptors such as malachite green (65).

Free radicals have been observed by electron spin resonance spectroscopy during dehydrogenation reactions which were catalysed by enzymes requiring NAD^+ (66). However, the signals were very weak and the reaction mixture was so complex that it is doubtful whether free radicals play an important part in dehydrogenation reactions which are catalysed by NAD^+.

Biochemical properties. The pyridine coenzymes, in association with appropriate protein apoenzymes, are cofactors for a wide variety of dehydrogenation reactions (67). One common dehydrogenation reaction, which is catalysed by NAD^+, is the oxidation of alcohols to aldehydes or ketones. The most important sources of alcohol dehydrogenases are yeast (59) and liver (68).

$$R_1CHOHR_2 + NAD^+ \rightleftharpoons R_1COR_2 + NADH$$

In addition to the oxidation of ethanol and other aliphatic primary and secondary alcohols, lactate (69), malate (70), and L-glycerol-1 phosphate (71) are all oxidized by dehydrogenases which require NAD^+.

Aldehydes (or their hydrates) are dehydrogenated to carboxylic acids by enzymes which require either NAD^+ or $NADP^+$ as co-factors (72, 73).

$$RCHO + NADP^+ \rightleftharpoons RCOOH + NADPH$$

Cyclic acetals, such as sugars and sugar phosphates, are dehydrogenated to lactones by similar enzymes (32, 74, 76).

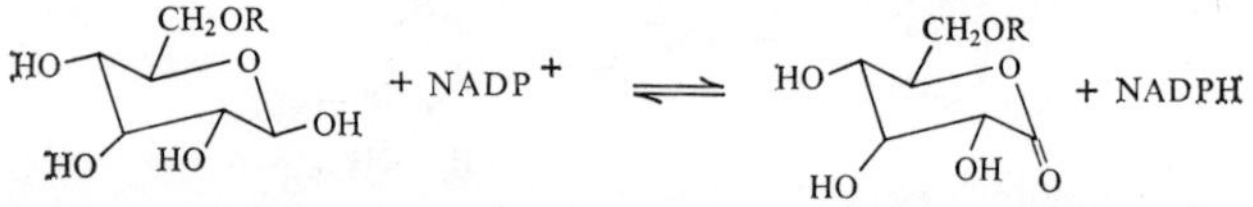

In the examples mentioned above, NAD^+ is acting as a catalyst for the transfer of hydride ions; however, NAD^+ is also a component of the electron-transferring cytochrome chain in mitochondria (76).

When a substrate is oxidized in a mitochondrion, electrons are transferred from the substrate along the cytochrome chain to molecular oxygen. NAD^+ is the first electron-transferring component in the chain and then transfers the electrons first to a flavoprotein, then to a series of cytochromes before the final transference of electrons to molecular oxygen takes place.

During the transference of one electron pair from the substrate to molecular oxygen three molecules of ATP are synthesized from ADP; this process is known as oxidative phosphorylation. While

$$\text{Substrate} \longrightarrow \text{NAD}^+ \xrightarrow[\text{ATP}]{\text{ADP}} \text{FAD} \longrightarrow \text{Cytochrome} \quad b \xrightarrow[\text{ATP}]{\text{ADP}} \text{Cytochrome} \quad c_1$$

$$O_2 \longleftarrow \text{Cytochrome} \quad a_3 \xleftarrow[\text{ATP}]{\text{ADP}} \text{Cytochrome} \quad a \longleftarrow \text{Cytochrome} \quad c$$

the exact nature of the process is unknown at the present time, mechanisms have been proposed which involve NAD^+ in oxidative phosphorylation (77). In one mechanism, the adenine ring of NAD^+ undergoes attack by a phosphate ion at the 2 carbon atom, and oxidation of the adduct by the flavoprotein gives adenyl-2 phosphate. Adenyl-2 phosphate then phosphorylates ADP to ATP. In another mechanism, a similar adduct is formed between phosphate and the nicotinamide ring of NAD^+; oxidation of this adduct by the flavoprotein again gives a highly reactive phosphorylating agent. Support for the latter mechanism is provided by the isolation from mitochondria of a phosphorylated NAD^+ derivative in which the pyridine ring is reduced (78). This phosphorylated NAD^+ derivative is capable of phosphorylating ADP to give ATP.

3.4 The flavin coenzymes

Introduction. The flavin coenzymes are oxidation-reduction co-enzymes by virtue of the reversible oxidation and reduction of the flavin moiety. In this respect they are similar to the nicotinamide coenzymes, and like the latter the flavin coenzymes can catalyse enzymic dehydrogenation reactions and are electron carriers in the cytochrome chain of mitochondria.

Riboflavin or Vitamin B_2 (XX) was one of the earliest vitamins to be recognized, isolated and studied. Free riboflavin occurs only in urine, whey, and in the retina of the eye; in all other systems it occurs in a phosphorylated form. Riboflavin itself has a very low activity as a coenzyme for enzymic dehydrogenation reactions; however, phosphate esters of riboflavin are very active catalysts in such reactions.

For example, one of the flavin coenzymes which will catalyse enzymic dehydrogenations is flavin-adenine dinucleotide (FAD) (XXI) which is a pyrophosphate ester of riboflavin.

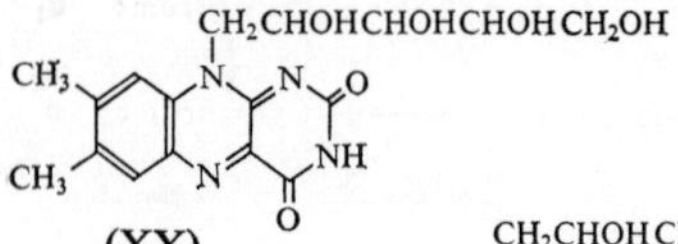

(XX)

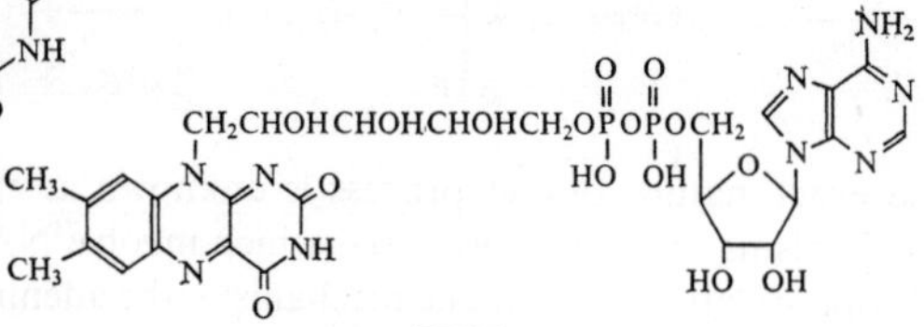

(XXI)

Riboflavin-5′ phosphate (XXII) is another of the flavin coenzymes.

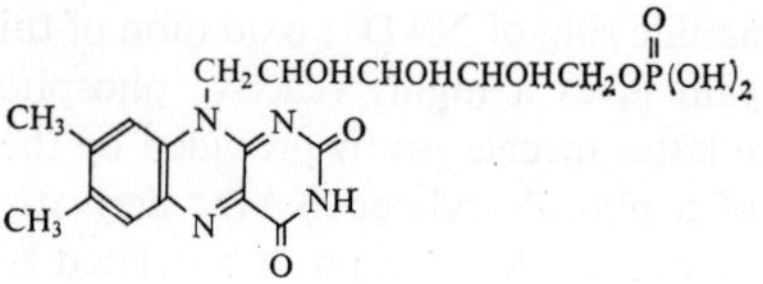

(XXII)

Determination of the structure of riboflavin. Acetylation of riboflavin gives a tetra-acetate, indicating the presence of four hydroxyl groups. These four hydroxyl groups must be in two adjacent pairs, as a di-isopropylidene derivative can be prepared from riboflavin and acetone in the presence of an acid as catalyst (79). Lead tetra-acetate will oxidize riboflavin to lumichrome, 6,7-dimethyl alloxazine. (XXIII) with the liberation of one equivalent of formaldehyde, hence a —CHOHCH$_2$OH group must be present in the molecule (80).

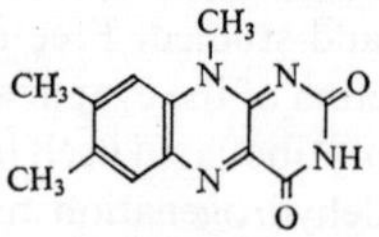

(XXIII)

Riboflavin is soluble in aqueous alkali, but the solution is unstable to light and lumiflavin (6,7,9-trimethyl isoalloxazine) (XXIV) is produced (81). Irradiation of riboflavin with ultraviolet light in neutral solution removes the ribityl side chain completely to give lumichrome (82). Riboflavin and lumiflavin are both isoalloxazines and have similar absorption spectra. Lumichrome, however, is an alloxazine and has a different absorption from the other two compounds.

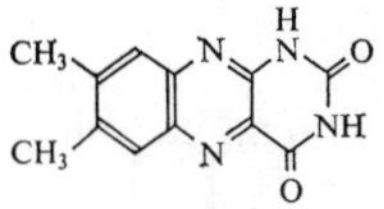

(XXIV)

Lumiflavin (XXIV) is hydrolysed by alkali to urea and 1,2-dihydro 1,6,7-trimethyl 2-keto 3-quinoxaline carboxylic acid (XXV). Decarboxylation of this carboxylic acid (XXV) followed by alkaline hydrolysis gives 1,2-dimethyl 4-amino 5-methylamino benzene (XXVI). Thus riboflavin is a glycoside of D-ribitol and 6,7-dimethy isoalloxazine, with the D-ribityl fragment attached to N_9 of the alloxazine moiety.

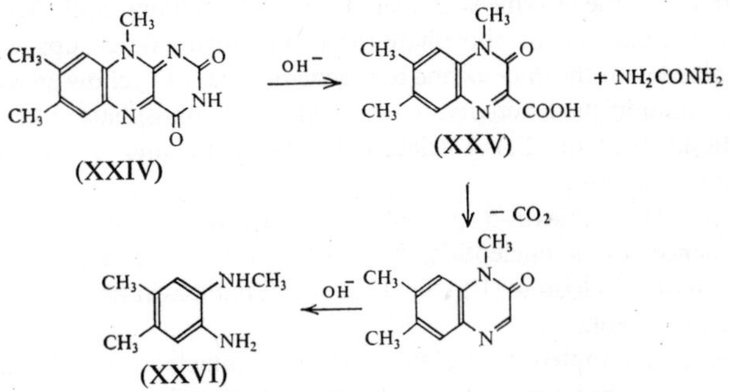

Riboflavin, lumichrome, and lumiflavin have all been synthesized by similar methods. For example, riboflavin has been prepared from 1,2-dimethyl 4-amino 5-(D-1′-ribitylamino) benzene (XXVII) and alloxan (XXVIII) in the presence of an acidic catalyst (83).

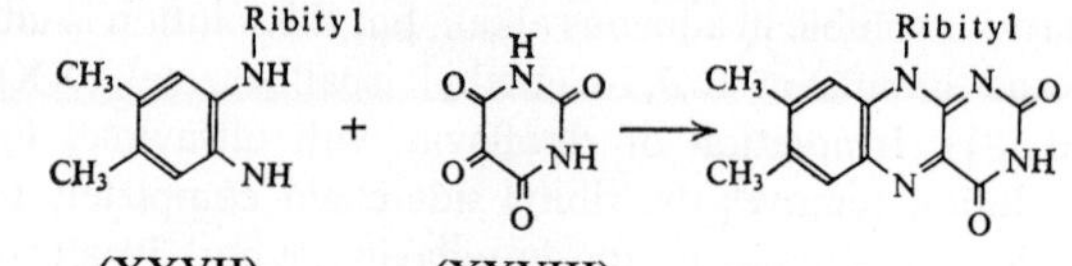

(XXVII)   (XXVIII)

The ribitylamino benzene (XXVII) can be prepared from ribose and 3,4-dimethyl aniline.

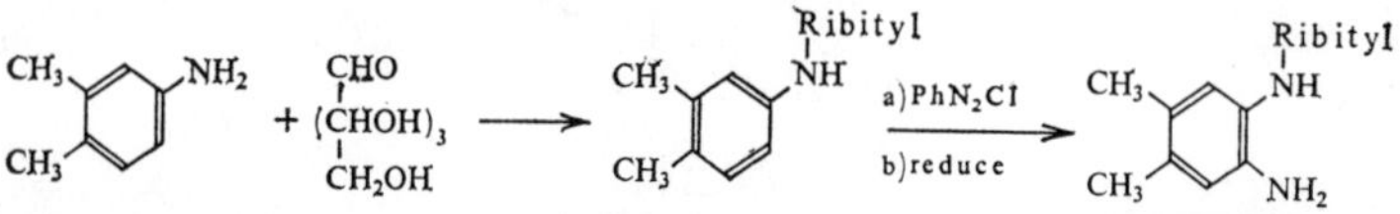

Structural determination of flavin nucleotides. A yellow, oxygen-transferring enzyme which contained riboflavin was isolated from yeast by Warburg and Christian in 1932 (84); this enzyme is now called the 'old yellow enzyme' as a second yellow enzyme with similar properties was isolated from yeast some six years later. The prosthetic group of the 'old yellow enzyme', which was isolated after treatment of the enzyme with methanol, contained one equivalent of riboflavin and one of phosphate (85). This prosthetic group, which combined with the apoenzyme to regenerate the 'old yellow enzyme' with undiminished activity, was riboflavin-5' phosphate and was synthesized from 2',3',4'-triacetoxy riboflavin and phosphorus oxychloride (86).

Although riboflavin-5' phosphate is not a derivative of D-ribose and hence not a nucleotide, it has acquired the trivial name of flavin mononucleotide (FMN). This trivial name will be retained in this Monograph.

Karrer attempted to isolate flavin mononucleotide from liver preparations, but was unable to obtain a pure sample of the coenzyme (87). The chief contaminant was an adenine nucleotide, which must have been released from a more complex form of FMN during the isolation procedure. This more complex form of FMN is now known to be flavin-adenine dinucleotide, and its function as the coenzyme of D-amino acid oxidase was first demonstrated by Warburg and Christian (88).

Flavin-adenine dinucleotide contains two equivalents of phosphate and liberates one equivalent of adenine after hydrolysis with acid. Photolysis of the coenzyme in alkaline solution gives one equivalent of lumiflavin. Careful hydrolysis with dilute acid liberates AMP and FMN in equivalent amounts (89). Thus, the coenzyme probably has the structure (XXI) which has been confirmed by synthesis.

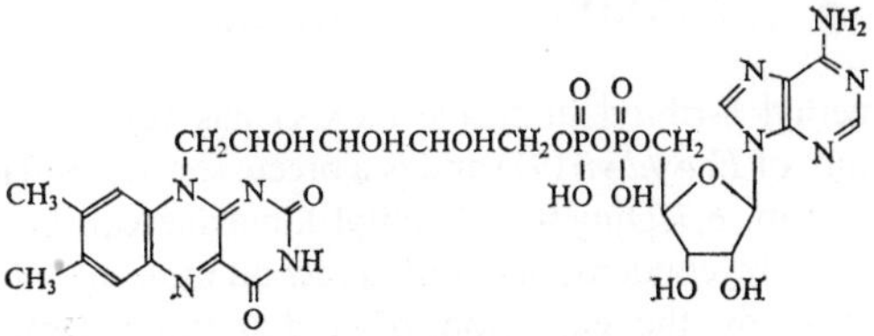

(XXI)

Synthesis of flavin-adenine dinucleotide. Several methods have been employed for the synthesis of FAD (90–93). In the synthesis by Khorana and Moffatt, the formation of the pyrophosphate bond was accomplished in high yield by the action of adenosine-5′ phosphoramidate on riboflavin-5′ phosphate (93).

Biosynthesis of Riboflavin, FMN, and FAD. While higher organisms depend on external sources for their supply of riboflavin, both bacteria and yeasts are able to synthesize the vitamin *ab initio*. The ascomycetes *Ashbya gossypii* and *Eremethecium ashbyii* produce riboflavin in such large amounts that these organisms are a commercial source of the vitamin.

If cells of either of these ascomycetes are grown in a medium which contains ^{14}C-formate, ^{14}C-carbon dioxide, ^{14}C-glycine and ^{15}N-glycine, the adenine and riboflavin which are produced have a very similar pattern of labelling (94). The incorporation of uniformly labelled ^{14}C-adenine into riboflavin by *E. ashbyii* and the concentration of the radioactive carbon atoms into the *o*-xylene and pyrazine rings of the riboflavin, provides evidence of a precursor-product relationship between adenine and riboflavin (95). The carbon atom in the 8 position of adenine is lost during the transformation into riboflavin (96); this suggests that both flavins and purines might have a common precursor. One such precursor might be a 5,6-diamino uracil (XXIX).

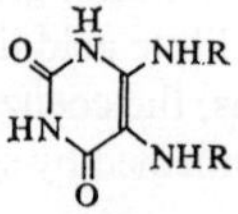

(XXIX) 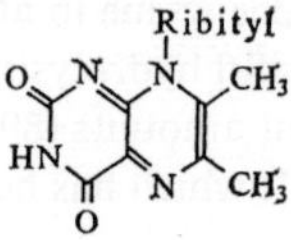   (XXX)

6,7-Dimethyl 8-ribityl lumazine (XXX) has been isolated from the mycelium of *E. ashbyii* (97) and is a precursor of riboflavin in this micro-organism. 6,7-Dimethyl 8-ribityl lumazine can be converted into riboflavin by condensation with a second molecule of the lumazine followed by the expulsion of a diamino pyrimidine (98). Diketones such as diacetyl are not involved in the conversion of the lumazine into riboflavin *in vivo* (99).

Riboflavin-5′ phosphate is formed enzymically by the phosphorylation of riboflavin by ATP in the presence of flavokinase (100).

$$\text{Riboflavin} + \text{ATP} \rightleftharpoons \text{FMN} + \text{ADP}$$

The riboflavin-5′ phosphate is then converted into FAD by a further phosphorylation with ATP (101).

$$\text{FMN} + \text{ATP} \rightleftharpoons \text{FAD} + \text{PP}_i$$

The reduction of flavin coenzymes. The redox potential at pH 7·1 and at 25°C for the system $FMN/FMNH_2$

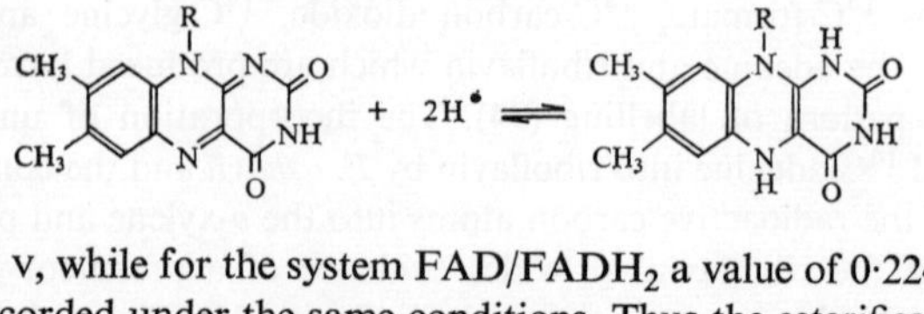

is 0·221 v, while for the system $FAD/FADH_2$ a value of 0·224 v has been recorded under the same conditions. Thus the esterification of the 5' phosphate group by an adenosine-5' phosphoryl residue makes little difference to the redox potential of the flavin coenzymes (102). The oxidation-reduction process *in vivo* is a free radical reaction (67, 103).

Biochemical functions. In most enzymic reactions, FMN and FAD are active only when they are bound to proteins. Little is known about the nature of the coenzyme-protein binding except that the phosphate group is probably involved at one of the binding sites (104).

The flavoproteins are oxidation-reduction coenzymes and, for example, can oxidize the reduced pyridine coenzymes, α-amino acids, aldehydes and purines. Flavoproteins can also reduce nitrate, nitrite, and hydroxylamine. In addition to their function as oxidation-reduction coenzymes, flavoproteins are electron carriers in the cytochrome chain in mitochondria.

When a substrate is oxidized by NAD^+ (or $NADP^+$), the reduced pyridine coenzyme (NADH or NADPH) is, necessarily, formed. The reduced pyridine coenzymes can be re-oxidized by a flavoprotein which then transfers its electrons to another electron carrier such as a cytochrome.

$$\text{Substrate}.H + NAD^+ \longrightarrow \text{Substrate} + NADH$$

$$2\,NADH + FMN \longrightarrow 2\,NAD^+ + FMNH_2$$

$$FMNH_2 + 2Fe^{III} \longrightarrow FMN + 2Fe^{II} + 2H^+$$

Enzymes which catalyse the oxidation of NADPH by ferricytochrome c have been isolated from yeast (105) and liver (106). In both cases the enzymes are flavoproteins, and in the yeast enzyme FMN is the prosthetic group; whereas in liver, FAD is the prosthetic group. Several reductases with similar properties have been detected in other sources (107) and electron acceptors such as quinones (Coenzyme Q) can function as substrates in this reaction (108).

Warburg's 'old yellow enzyme' is a D-α-amino acid oxidase, and the mechanism for the oxidation of both D- and L-α-amino acids appears to be similar (109). The reaction is thought to be a three-stage process: (i) the amino acid is oxidized to an imine, (ii) the imine is hydrolysed, and (iii) FAD regenerated from $FADH_2$ by electron transfer to molecular oxygen.

(i) $NH_2CHRCOOH + FAD \longrightarrow FADH_2 + NH{=}CRCOOH$

(ii) $NH{=}CHRCOOH + H_2O \longrightarrow NH_3 + RCOCOOH$

(iii) $2 FADH_2 + O_2 \longrightarrow 2 FAD + H_2O$

The oxidation of purines, such as hypoxanthine and xanthine, to uric acid is one of the last stages in the catabolism of nucleic acids. Xanthine oxidase is a flavoprotein which requires iron and molybdenum for its activity (103). The enzyme has, however, a very low substrate and electron acceptor specificity, being able to oxidize NADH and aldehydes (110), and can transfer electrons to such different compounds as methylene blue, oxygen, quinones, and ferricyanide (111).

The reduction of nitrate to nitrite by NADPH in *Neurospora crassa* is brought about by a flavoprotein which requires both FAD and molybdenum as cofactors (112). A similar enzyme system which reduces nitrite to ammonia has been detected in *Escherichia Coli* (113). The latter enzyme system is unable to reduce nitrous oxide, hyponitrite or nitrate, but will rapidly reduce hydroxylamine. Experiments with ^{15}N labelled nitrite indicate, however, that free hydroxylamine is not an obligatory intermediate in this reaction.

A living organism obtains its energy from the oxidation of the metabolites of carbohydrates, proteins, and fats. Under aerobic conditions these metabolites transfer electrons during the oxidative process to molecular oxygen through a series of electron carriers which are known as the cytochrome chain. During the transfer of two electrons from the substrate to molecular oxygen, ATP is synthesized from ADP and this process is known as oxidative phosphorylation.

The exact composition of the cytochrome chain is uncertain at the present time, and at least two distinct electron transferring chains are proposed depending on the substrate undergoing oxidation. In one, the substrate transfers its electron pair to NAD$^+$ which then transfers the electron pair first to a flavoprotein, then to a series of cytochromes of decreasing oxidation-reduction potential until the final transference to molecular oxygen is achieved (76).

(I) ....Substrate $\rightarrow$ NAD$^+$ $\rightarrow$ flavoprotein $\rightarrow$ cyt. b $\rightarrow$ cyt. c_1

with ADP/ATP at the NAD$^+$ step and the cyt. b step, and:

$$O_2 \leftarrow \text{cyt. } a_3 \leftarrow \text{cyt. } a \leftarrow \text{cyt. } c$$

with ADP/ATD at the cyt. a step.

During the passage of an electron pair along this chain, three molecules of ATP are synthesized, one at each of the steps shown above. The prosthetic group of the flavoprotein in this chain appears to be FAD (114). Earlier reports that FMN is the prosthetic group in this flavoprotein are probably due to the degradation of the FAD to FMN during the isolation procedure, as the flavin nucleotide is very tightly bound to the protein. Succinate is dehydrogenated by a second cytochrome chain (76); in this case, the succinate transfers its electron pair directly to a flavoprotein without the intermediacy of NAD$^+$. The flavoprotein then transfers the electron pair to molecular oxygen through a series of cytochromes. Only two molecules of ATP are synthesized from ADP during this process.

(II) ....Substrate $\longrightarrow$ flavoprotein $\rightarrow$ cyt. b $\rightarrow$ cyt. c_1

with ADP/ATP at the cyt. b step, and:

$$O_2 \leftarrow \text{cyt. } a_3 \leftarrow \text{cyt. } a \leftarrow \text{cyt. } c$$

with ADP/ATP at the cyt. a step.

While the flavoprotein of succinic dehydrogenase (Type II) differs from the flavoprotein of the NAD$^+$ linked dehydrogenase (Type I), the prosthetic group appears to be the same in both cases (115).

Two proposals for the phosphorylation process in the NAD$^+$-flavoprotein step have already been mentioned in the previous section; in a third proposal, one of the oxygen atoms of the flavin moiety is phosphorylated. Under oxidative conditions, this phosphorylated flavin would transfer its phosphate group to ADP (116).

5

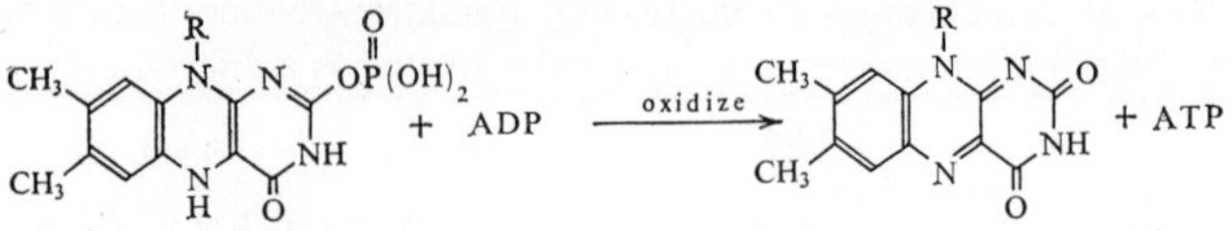

3.5 Coenzyme A

Discovery. During his investigations on acetyl phosphate (XXXI), Lipmann observed that although pigeon liver extracts lost their ability to acetylate sulphanilamide (XXXII) after dialysis, the activity was restored after the addition of boiled liver extracts (117). This behaviour is characteristic of a heat stable coenzyme-apoenzyme system, the coenzyme being removed by dialysis and restored by the addition of the boiled liver extracts. Lipmann called this coenzyme Coenzyme A (CoA), and showed it to be a constituent of most living organisms (118).

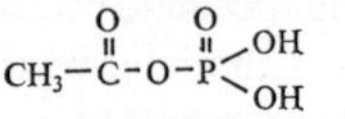

In contrast to the pyridine and flavin coenzymes, which function in oxidation-reduction reactions, Coenzyme A is an acyl-transferring coenzyme and is the cofactor for a wide variety of biological acylations. For example, the synthesis of acetoacetate from acetate and ATP in pigeon liver is catalysed by CoA. The acetoacetate is formed from TWO activated two carbon fragments (both of which are derived from acetyl phosphate) and is not formed by the acetylation of the methyl group of an acetate molecule (119).

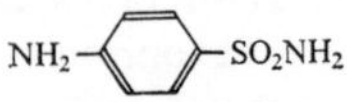

Although CoA was originally isolated from fresh liver, the inconvenience of handling large amounts of fresh liver has led to the development of micro-organisms such as yeast as more convenient sources of the coenzyme.

Structural determination. The structure of Coenzyme A (XXXIII) was elucidated as a result of the work of Baddiley (120), Lipmann (121), and Snell (122). The structure was confirmed by the total synthesis of CoA by Khorana (123), Michelson (124), and Lynen (125).

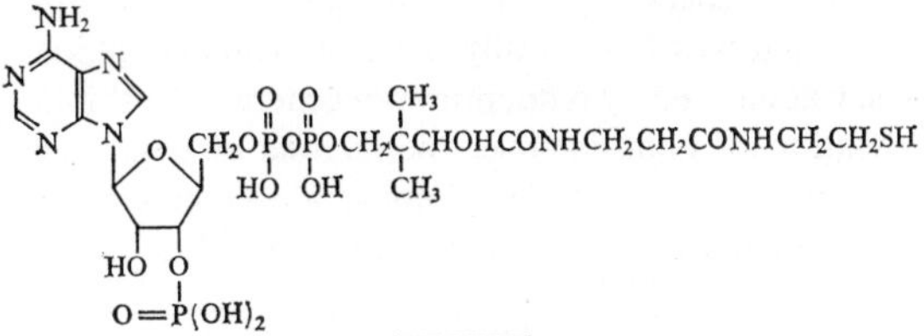

(XXXIII)

Degradation by specific enzymes has been the most useful tool in the structural determination of CoA. The first step was the isolation of pantothenic acid (XXXIV) from CoA after treatment with papain, a proteolytic enzyme (126). Lipmann and co-workers showed that in addition to pantothenic acid, CoA, after treatment with alkaline phosphatase, liberated adenosine, three equivalents of phosphate and a sulphur-containing compound (127).

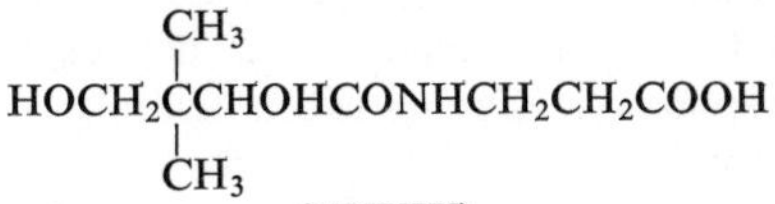

$$\begin{array}{c} CH_3 \\ | \\ HOCH_2CCHOHCONHCH_2CH_2COOH \\ | \\ CH_3 \end{array}$$

(XXXIV)

$$\begin{array}{c} CH_3 \\ | \\ HOCH_2CCHOHCONHCH_2CH_2CONHCH_2CH_2SH \\ | \\ CH_3 \end{array}$$

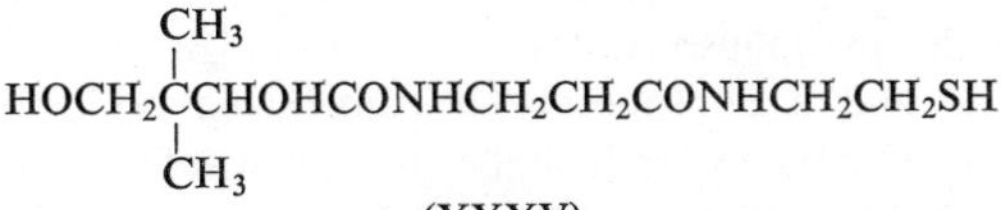

(XXXV)

Pantothenic acid is a member of the B group of vitamins, and its structure and chemistry have been reviewed by Snell (128).

When CoA was treated with an intestinal phosphatase, the *Lactobacillus bulgaricus* growth factor was released (129). This is pantothenic acid joined by an amide linkage to 2-mercapto ethylamine, and is now called panthetheine (XXXV) (130).

Acidic hydrolysis of CoA liberated all the sulphur present in the coenzyme in the form of 2-mercapto ethylamine (131).

Aerial oxidation of pantetheine gave the disulphide, which was called pantethine by analogy with the amino acids cysteine and cystine. Similarly the coenzyme itself readily underwent oxidation to the disulphide which was biologically inactive. The disulphide link, in both cases, was cleaved by reduction to regenerate the thiol.

Condensation of pantolactone, the lactone of pantothenic acid, with N-β-alanyl 2-mercapto ethylamine gave pantetheine, which proved the structure of pantetheine (132).

The next problem to be resolved by specific enzymic hydrolysis was the positions of the three phosphate groups. Prostatic phosphatase, a phosphomonoesterase, denatured CoA with the liberation of one equivalent of orthophosphate and 'dephospho CoA' (133). A specific phosphomonoesterase which hydrolysed nucleoside-3' phosphates, but not nucleoside-2' or -5' phosphates, also degraded CoA to 'dephospho CoA' and one equivalent of orthophosphate (134). Thus CoA is a derivative of adenosine-3' phosphate.

Nucleoside pyrophosphatases cleave CoA to adenosine-3',5' diphosphate and a phosphorylated pantetheine (135, 136). The phosphorylated pantetheine is similar to a growth factor for *Acetobacter suboxydans* which has been isolated from heart muscle. The growth factor was thought to be a 'simple' phosphate of pantothenic acid. However, when pantothenic acid -2 and -4 phosphates were prepared together with the -2,4 cyclic phosphate and the -2,4 diphosphate, all were inactive as growth factors for the micro-organism (137). Pantetheine-4 phosphate was identical with the growth factor and was converted into CoA in the presence of ATP by a liver enzyme (137). Pantetheine-2 phosphate and the -2,4 cyclic phosphate were not converted into CoA by this enzyme. Pantetheine-4 phosphate was prepared by the direct phosphorylation of pantethine with dibenzyl phosphorochloridate, followed by the simultaneous removal of the benzyl groups and cleavage of the disulphide link by reduction with sodium in liquid ammonia (137).

From the above evidence the structure (XXXIII) was proposed for Coenzyme A, and the structure (XXXVI) was proposed for 'dephospho Coenzyme A'.

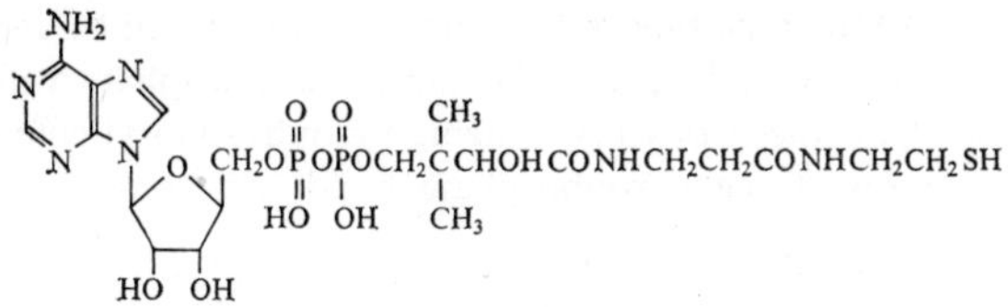

(XXXVI)

Synthesis. Three methods have been employed for the formation of the pyrophosphate bond in CoA.

In Khorana's total synthesis of the coenzyme, pantetheine-4 phosphate was coupled with a suitably substituted adenosine-5′ phosphoramidate (123). 'Dephospho CoA' was obtained from the reaction between pantetheine-4 phosphate and adenosine-5′ phosphoromorpholidate. Adenosine-3′ phosphate-5′ phosphoromorpholidate could not be used for the synthesis of the coenzyme as there would be competition for the phosphoromorpholidate between the adenosine-3′ phosphate and the pantetheine-4 phosphate. However, when adenosine-2′,3′ cyclic phosphate-5′ phosphoromorpholidate (XXXVII) was treated with pantetheine-4 phosphate, and the cyclic phosphate opened with acid, a mixture of CoA and isoCoA

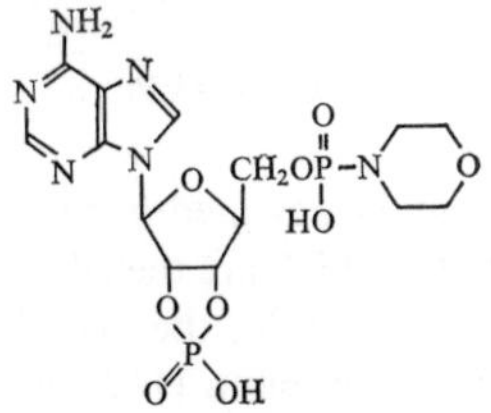

(XXXVII)

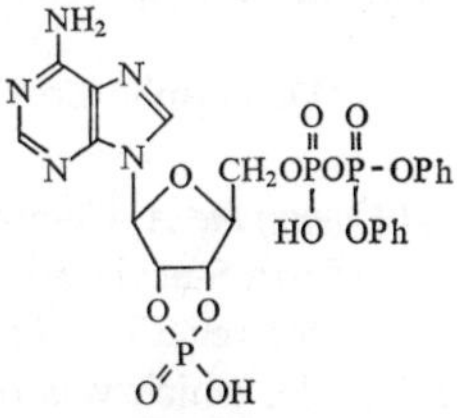

(XXXVIII)

(the adenosine-2′ phosphate derivative) were obtained. These isomers were then separated by chromatography on ion-exchange cellulose. The success of this method depended on the preferential attack by a phosphomonoester rather than a phosphodiester on the phosphoromorpholidate.

A better yield of CoA was obtained by Michelson (124) from P^1-adenosine-2′,3′ cyclic phosphate-5′-P^2-diphenyl pyrophosphate (XXXVIII) and pantethine-4,4′ diphosphate, followed by reduction of the disulphide and opening of the cyclic phosphate with ribonuclease. A synthesis of CoA utilizing pyrophosphoryl chloride for the formation of the pyrophosphate bond has been reported by Lynen (125).

Biosynthesis. The main biosynthetic route to CoA in most animals appears to be the following (138). Pantothenic acid is phosphorylated by ATP to pantothenic acid-4 phosphate; this then reacts with β-alanine in the presence of either ATP or CTP to give pantetheine-4 phosphate. The phosphorylated pantetheine then reacts with ATP to produce the adenosine-pantetheine pyrophosphate 'dephospho CoA', together with inorganic phosphate. The 'dephospho CoA' is then phosphorylated on the 3′ hydroxyl of the adenosine moiety by ATP.

$$\text{Pantothenic acid} + \text{ATP} \longrightarrow \text{pantothenic acid-4 phosphate} + \text{ADP}$$

$$\text{Pantothenic acid-4 phosphate} + \beta\text{-alanine} \xrightarrow[\text{ATP}]{\text{CTP}} \text{pantetheine-4 phosphate}$$

$$\text{Pantetheine-4 phosphate} + \text{ATP} \longrightarrow \text{'dephospho CoA'}$$

$$\text{'Dephospho CoA'} + \text{ATP} \longrightarrow \text{CoA} + \text{PP}_i$$

S-Acyl Coenzyme A. Coenzyme A can be acylated *in vitro* without difficulty to form S-acyl derivatives (139) which are the active species in acyl transfer reactions *in vivo*. For example, the acetylation of sulphanilamide, which was observed by Lipmann (117), is brought about by S-acetyl CoA. The S-acetyl CoA is formed by the reaction between CoA and acetyl phosphate; the latter is a mixed anhydride of acetic and phosphoric acids and is consequently a good acetylating agent.

$$CoASH + CH_3\overset{O}{\underset{\|}{C}}{-}O{-}\overset{O}{\underset{\|}{P}}(OH)_2 \longrightarrow CoAS{-}COCH_3 + P_i$$

'Active acetate', the acetylating agent in reactions which are catalysed by Lipmann's enzyme system, has been isolated and identified as S-acetyl CoA by Lynen and co-workers (140).

S-Acetyl CoA is stable to heat and acids but is hydrolysed in alkaline solution. This reaction is a general one for S-acyl thiols and has been adapted by Lynen for the estimation of S-acetyl CoA. This estimation method depends on the determination of the purple colour which is slowly produced when S-acetyl CoA is treated with an alkaline solution of nitroprusside. The purple colour arises from the interaction between the nitroprusside and free CoA, which is slowly liberated by the alkaline hydrolysis of the S-acetyl CoA.

$$CoAS\overset{O}{\underset{\|}{C}}CH_3 + OH^{(-)} \xrightarrow{\text{H}_2\text{O}} CoASH + CH_3COOH$$

Acetate is also removed from S-acetyl CoA by the action of mercuric salts; the products of this reaction are acetic acid and the mercuric mercaptan of CoA. The latter can be decomposed by hydrogen sulphide to give pure CoA.

S-Acyl thiols are acylating agents because they are mixed anhydrides of thiols and carboxylic acids. Nucleophilic attack on the electron-deficient carbon atom of the carbonyl group, followed by the expulsion of the thiol, leads to the formation of the acylated nucleophile.

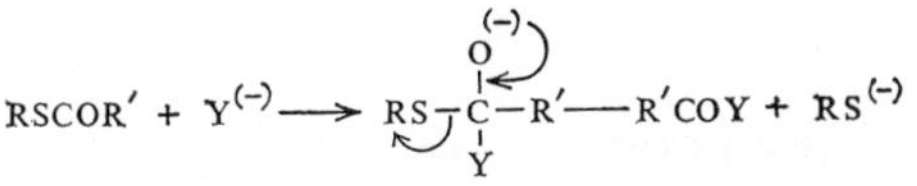

$$RSCOR' + Y^{(-)} \longrightarrow RS{-}\overset{O^{(-)}}{\underset{\underset{Y}{|}}{C}}{-}R' \longrightarrow R'COY + RS^{(-)}$$

This is one way in which S-acyl thiols can react. A second way is by the formation of an anion on the carbon atom α to the carbonyl group. This anion can then react with electrophiles such as carbonyl groups.

$$RSCOCH_2R' \xrightarrow{\text{base}} RSCOCHR'^{(-)} \xrightarrow{Z^+} RSCOCHR'^{Z}$$

In the synthesis of S-acetoacetyl CoA from two molecules of S-acetyl CoA (119), both these reaction paths are used. The carbanion of one molecule of S-acetyl CoA adds on to the carbonyl group of the second molecule of S-acetyl CoA. The expulsion of one molecule of CoA leads to the formation of S-acetoacetyl CoA.

$$CoASCOCH_3 + CoASCOCH_2^{(-)} \longrightarrow CoASCOCH_2COCH_3 + CoAS^{(-)}$$

The reactions of S-acyl CoA derivatives in biological systems. The enzymic acylation of amines by S-acyl CoA derivatives is an example of a reaction proceeding by nucleophilic attack on the carbonyl group of the S-acyl CoA.

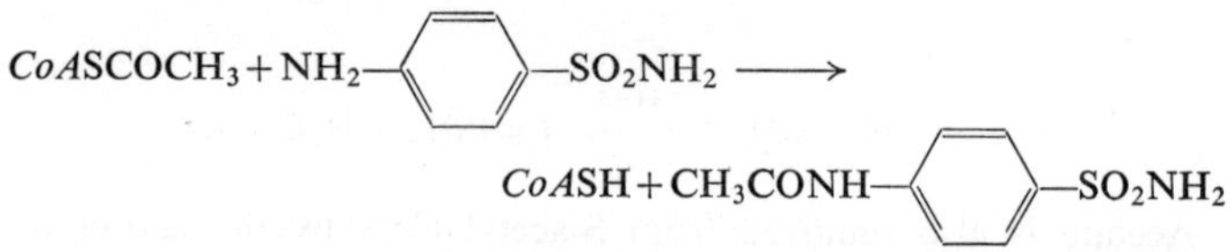

$$CoASCOCH_3 + NH_2\text{---}\langle\bigcirc\rangle\text{---}SO_2NH_2 \longrightarrow$$

$$CoASH + CH_3CONH\text{---}\langle\bigcirc\rangle\text{---}SO_2NH_2$$

Aromatic amines are not the only substrates for this type of reaction and aliphatic amines such as amino acids and glucosamines are acetylated by S-acetyl CoA *in vivo* (141). The attacking nucleophile can also be hydroxyl groups or ions (142), carboxylate ions (143), or phosphate ions (144). The reaction between S-acetyl CoA and inorganic phosphate is reversible, the products being acetyl phosphate and CoA.

$$CoASCOCH_3 + ROH \longrightarrow CoASH + RCOOCH_3$$

$$CoASCOCH_3 + RCOO^- \longrightarrow CoASCOR + CH_3COO^-$$

$$CoASCOCH_3 + P_i \rightleftharpoons CoASH + CH_3\underset{\underset{O}{\|}}{C}O\underset{\underset{O}{\|}}{P}(OH)_2$$

In the enzymic reduction of S-palmityl CoA by NADPH, the first step is probably the addition of a hydride ion to the electron deficient carbonyl group of the S-palmityl CoA. This is then followed by the elimination of the anion of CoA to leave palmityl aldehyde (145).

$$CoASCR + H^{(-)} \rightleftharpoons CoASC—R \rightleftharpoons CoAS^{(-)} + RCHO$$

The formation of citrate and malate from S-acetyl CoA and the appropriate carbonyl compound (oxalacetate and glyoxalate respectively) are reactions which proceed by the initial formation of the carbonion of S-acetyl CoA, and hence are analogous to aldol condensations.

$$\begin{matrix} CO.COOH \\ | \\ CH_2COOH \end{matrix} + CoASCOCH_2{}^{(-)} \longrightarrow CoAS^{(-)} + \begin{matrix} CH_2.COOH \\ | \\ COH.COOH \\ | \\ CH_2.COOH \end{matrix}$$

$$\begin{matrix} CHO \\ | \\ COOH \end{matrix} + CoASCOCH_2 \longrightarrow CoAS^{(-)} + \begin{matrix} CH_2.COOH \\ | \\ CHOH.COOH \end{matrix}$$

Coenzyme A in the synthesis of fatty acids. S-Malonyl CoA is an important intermediate in the biosynthesis of fatty acids. The precursors of S-malonyl CoA are bicarbonate and S-acetyl CoA, the reaction being catalysed by biotin.

$$CoASCOCH_3 + HCO_3{}^- \xrightarrow{\text{biotin}} CoASCOCH_2COOH$$

The mechanism of this reaction has been the subject of controversy. Recently, Waite and Wakil (146) have proposed that the bicarbonate is incorporated into enzyme-bound biotin (XXXIX) as the ureido carbon atom. The N-carboxyl biotin derivative (XL), formed from biotin by the opening of the ureido ring, is thought to be the reactive carboxylating agent and could convert S-acetyl CoA into S-malonyl CoA.

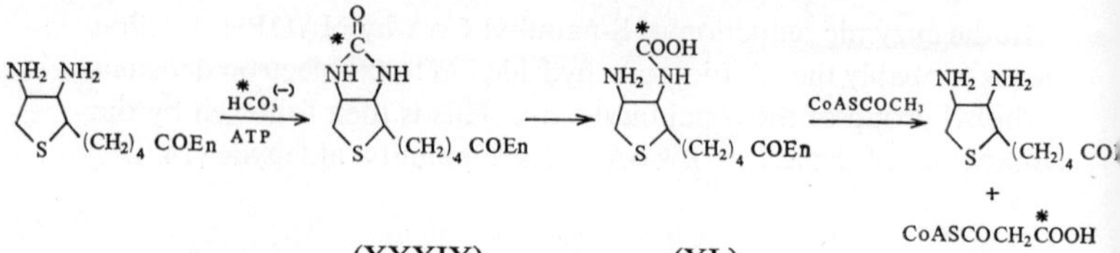

(XXXIX)   (XL)

(where En is the transcarboxylase enzyme)

However, a transcarboxylase has been isolated which contains biotin, and this biotin can be labelled at the ureido carbon atom with ^{14}C (147). The ^{14}C labelled biotin does not lose a significant amount of radioactivity during the carboxylation of S-propionyl CoA to S-methyl malonyl CoA. The reactive intermediate is believed to be N-carboxyl biotin (XLI) in which the ureido ring is intact.

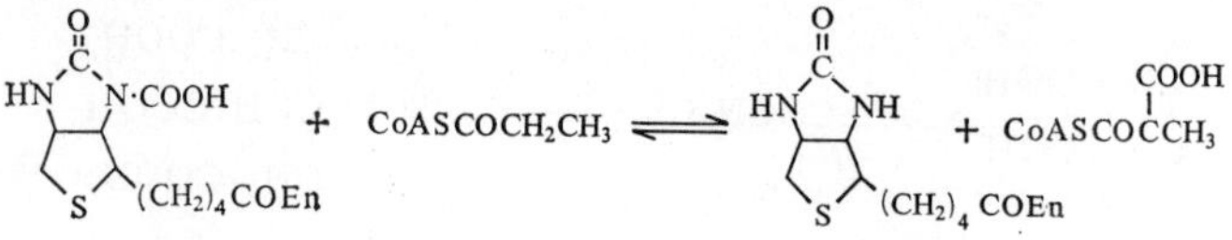

(XLI)   (XXXIX)

(where En is the transcarboxylase enzyme)

This experiment provides support for the mechanism proposed by Lynen (148) for transcarboxylation reactions. In Lynen's mechanism the biotin reacts with bicarbonate and ATP to produce the N-carboxyl biotin (XLI) which is the active species in this type of reaction.

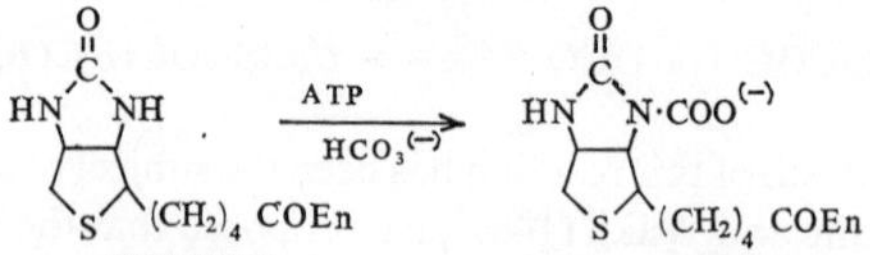

(XXXIX)   (XLI)

N-carboxy biotin (XLI) has been isolated from this reaction as its dimethyl ester (148). In addition, β-methyl crotonyl carboxylase (149), propionyl carboxylase (150), and oxaloacetic transcarboxylase

(151) all react with ^{14}C labelled bicarbonate to give enzyme-bound N-^{14}C carboxyl biotin.

Thus it appears that Lynen's mechanism for the incorporation of bicarbonate into biotin, followed by the carboxylation of S-acyl CoA derivatives, is correct

When S-malonyl CoA is incubated with S-acetyl CoA and NADPH in the presence of a liver enzyme, palmitate is produced from *one* molecule of S-acetyl CoA and *seven* molecules of S-malonyl CoA (152).

$$CoASCOCH_3 + 7\ CoASCOCH_2COOH \longrightarrow$$
$$CoASCO(CH_2)_{14}CH_3 + 7\ CoASH + 7\ CO_2$$

If the S-acetyl CoA is replaced by S-propionyl CoA, or S-butyryl CoA, fatty acids are produced which contain 17 and 18 carbon atoms respectively (153). In the latter case the fatty acid is stearic acid, and both fatty acids are formed from *seven* molecules of S-malonyl CoA and *one* molecule of the S-acyl CoA derivative.

The S-malonyl CoA–S-acyl CoA enzyme system appears to be the major biosynthetic route to fatty acids in living organism as the enzyme system has been detected in animal, insect, and plant tissues.

Coenzyme A in fatty acid catabolism. When fatty acids are degraded enzymically in the presence of CoA under aerobic conditions, one of the final products is S-acetyl CoA. The enzymic reactions have been studied in detail for butyrate, and five separate processes are involved (154). The butyrate is first converted into S-butyryl CoA which is then dehydrogenated by a flavoprotein to the unsaturated S-crotonyl CoA.

$$CH_3CH_2CH_2COOH + CoASH \longrightarrow CoASCOCH_2CH_2CH_3$$

$$CoASCOCH_2CH_2CH_3 \xrightarrow{\text{flavoprotein}} CoASCOCH{=}CHCH_3$$

The carbon-carbon double bond of S-crotonyl CoA is then hydrated to give S-β-hydroxybutyryl CoA, which is then dehydrogenated by NAD$^+$ to S-acetoacetyl CoA.

$$CoA\text{SCOCH}=\text{CHCH}_3 \xrightarrow{\text{H}_2\text{O}} CoA\text{SCOCH}_2\text{CHOHCH}_3$$

$$CoA\text{SCOCH}_2\text{CHOHCH}_3 \xrightarrow{\text{NAD}^+} CoA\text{SCOCH}_2\text{COCH}_3$$

The S-acetoacetyl CoA then reacts with a molecule of CoA to give, finally, two molecules of S-acetyl CoA.

$$CoA\text{SCOCH}_2\text{COCH}_3 + CoA\text{SH} \longrightarrow 2\ CoA\text{SCOCH}_3$$

Fatty acid S-acyl CoA derivatives are intermediate in the biosynthesis of fats and phospholipids. This aspect of their biochemistry will be discussed in detail in the next section.

3.6 Nucleoside diphosphate sugars

Nucleoside diphosphate sugars play an important part in the metabolism of sugars and in the biosynthesis of oligo- and polysaccharides. The commonest nucleoside diphosphate sugars are those which contain either the pyrimidine nucleoside uridine, or the purine nucleoside guanosine. Only one adenosine and a few thymidine diphosphate sugars have been reported at the present time. Cytidine diphosphate coenzymes which contain ethanolamine, choline, glycerol, and ribitol are coenzymes in the biosynthesis of bacterial cell walls and phospholipids. Although such coenzymes are not nucleoside diphosphate sugars, they will be described in this section for convenience.

Uridine diphosphate sugars. Uridine diphosphate glucose (UDPG) (XLII) was the first nucleotide coenzyme to be discovered which did not contain adenosine in the nucleoside moiety.

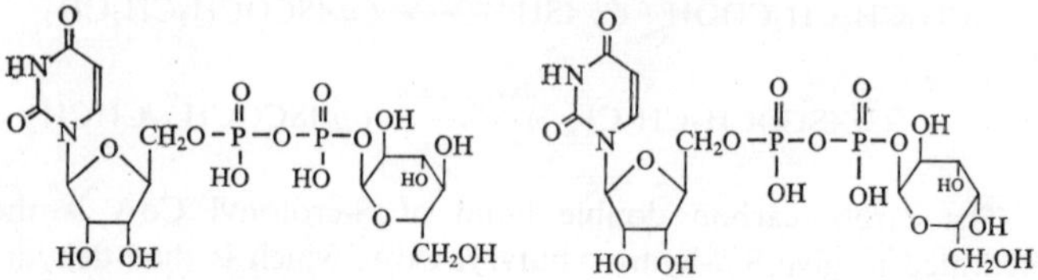

(XLII)   (XLIII)

UDPG was discovered by Leloir during his studies on the metabolism of galactose in yeast (155). D-Galactose is first converted by ATP, into D-galactose-1 phosphate; the latter then reacts with UDPG to give D-glucose-1 phosphate and UDP-galactose (UDPGal) (XLIII).

$$\text{galactose} + \text{ATP} \longrightarrow \text{galactose-1 phosphate} + \text{ADP}$$

$$\text{galactose-1 phosphate} + \text{UDPG} \longrightarrow \text{glucose-1 phosphate} + \text{UDPGal}$$

Acid hydrolysis of UDPG gave UMP, inorganic orthophosphate, and glucose (155); mild acid hydrolysis gave UDP and glucose. Electrometric titration indicated the presence of two primary phosphoric acid dissociations but no secondary dissociation. Thus the compound was probably a uridine-5′ sugar pyrophosphate. The position of attachment of the pyrophosphate group to the glucose moiety was probably the 1-carbon atom, owing to the extreme lability of the sugar-pyrophosphate bond. This was confirmed by the isolation of glucose-1,2 cyclic phosphate after the alkaline hydrolysis of UDPG (156). The configuration of the glycosidic glucose-1 pyrophosphate bond could be either α- or β-, as both the α- and β-anomers of glucose-1 phosphate cyclize to give the same product (157).

The final structural proof, and in particular the configuration of the glucose-1 pyrophosphate linkage came from the chemical (93, 158, 159) and enzymic (161, 162) syntheses of the coenzyme. *In vitro*, UDPG has been synthesized in high yield from uridine-5′ phosphoramidate and α-D-glucose-1 phosphate (93). *In vivo* UDPG is synthesized from UTP and α-D-glucose-1 phosphate (160, 161); this is the typical enzymic route to nucleoside pyrophosphate esters.

$$\alpha\text{-D-glucose-1 phosphate} + \text{UTP} \longrightarrow \text{UDPG} + \text{PP}$$

UDPGal has also been synthesized chemically (159), and like most of the nucleoside diphosphate sugars is synthesized enzymically from UTP and the appropriate α-D-sugar-1 phosphate (162).

UDPGal is reconverted into UDPG by an enzyme 'galactowaldenase'. This enzyme catalyses the Walden inversion of the 4-hydroxyl group of the sugar from the axial position in galactose (XLIV) to the equatorial position in glucose (XLVI).

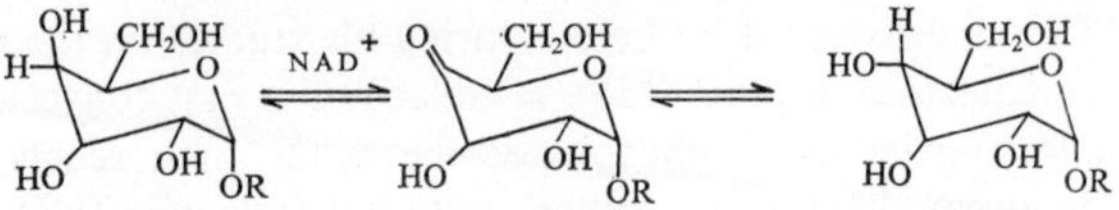

The inversion reaction probably proceeds by way of the 4-keto sugar (XLV) as NAD^+ is a cofactor for this enzyme (163). The equatorial position is the most stable configuration for the hydroxyl group, and hence the equilibrium ratio of glucose to galactose is $3:1$.

In addition to its function as a coenzyme for galactose metabolism in yeast, UDPG is also involved in the biosynthesis of disaccharides such as sucrose phosphate from UDPG and fructose or fructose-6 phosphate (164, 165).

$$UDPG + fructose \longrightarrow sucrose + UDP$$

$$UDPG + fructose\text{-}6\ phosphate \longrightarrow sucrose\ phosphate + UDP$$

The fructose can be replaced in this reaction by a number of other hexoses such as D-xylulose or L-sorbose to give the corresponding disaccharide. Similarly, D-lactose-1 phosphate is formed fom UDPGal and glucose-1 phosphate (166).

Both starch and glycogen are synthesized *in vivo* from UDPG. The overall reaction for glycogen may be written as follows:

$$x(UDPG) + (\alpha\text{-}1,4\text{-}D\text{-}glucose)_n \longrightarrow (\alpha\text{-}1,4\text{-}D\text{-}glucose)_{n+x} + xUDP$$

The reaction resembles the biosynthesis of polynucleotides, which is catalysed by polynucleotide phosphorylase, as a similar linkage is formed and a similar primer is required before the reaction will take place. The reverse reaction also takes place, and glycogen can be degraded enzymically to D-glucose-1 phosphate.

Several other uridine diphosphate sugars have been isolated, in addition to UDPG and UDPGal; among those reported are UDP-D-glucuronic acid (167), UDP-D-galacturonic acid (168), UDP-N-acetyl-D-glucosamine (169), UDP-N-acetyl-D-galactosamine (169), UDP-D-xylose and UDP-L-arabinose (170). All these compounds appear to be involved in the biosynthesis of oligo- and polysaccharides.

For example, hyaluronic acid, which is an unbranched poly-saccharide composed of alternating β-1,4 linked N-acetyl D-gluco-samine and β-1,3 linked D-glucuronic acid, requires both UDP-D-glucuronic acid and UDP-N-acetyl D-glucosamine as cofactors for its synthesis (171). However, no cell-free systems have been prepared up to the present time in which such biosynthetic reactions have been observed.

The sugar moieties of the various uridine diphosphate sugars are all α-anomers; in some oligo- and polysaccharides the α-configuration is retained while in others inversion has occurred. If the substrate which reacts with the UDP sugar is a carbohydrate, the reaction always proceeds with retention of configuration. However, if the substrate is a sugar phosphate, retention of configuration (sucrose, glycogen) or inversion of configuration (maltose, cellobiose) may take place. These observations can be explained by assuming that the reaction takes place by a S_N2 mechanism on the enzyme surface (172). Thus, the displacing group attacks the asymmetric carbon atom of the sugar from the opposite side to that bearing the leaving group (UDP), and the product has a β-configuration.

$$\text{UDP-}\alpha\text{-D-glucose} + S \longrightarrow \text{UDP} + \text{S-}\beta\text{-D-glucose}$$

When retention of configuration occurs, it is thought that a double inversion takes place: first an 'active' group in the enzyme displaces the UDP residue, then the enzyme-sugar complex undergoes a second S_N2 displacement with the sugar substrate.

$$\text{UDP-}\alpha\text{-D-glucose} + \text{En} \longrightarrow \text{UDP} + \text{En-}\beta\text{-D-glucose}$$

$$\text{En-}\beta\text{-D-glucose} + S \longrightarrow \text{En} + \text{S-}\alpha\text{-D-glucose}$$

Guanosine diphosphate sugars. Guanosine diphosphate D-mannose (GDPM) (XLVII) was first isolated from a mixture of nucleotides which had been obtained from yeast (173), and its structure was proved by a series of degradative experiments similar to those described for UDPG. The enzymic synthesis from GTP and α-D-mannose-1 phosphate follows the normal pattern (174). Other guanosine diphosphate sugars which have been isolated from various sources include GDP-D-glucose (175), GDP-D-fructose (176) and GDP-L-fucose (176).

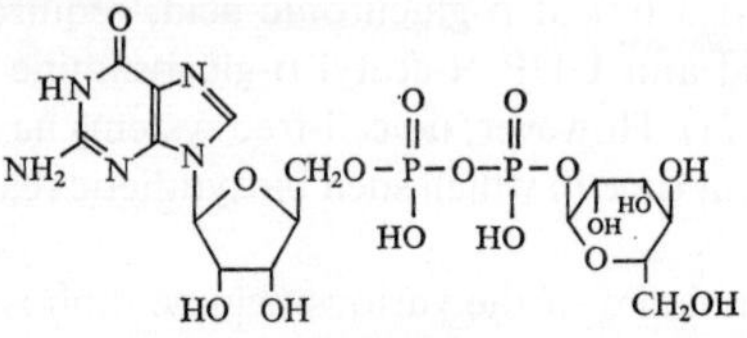

(XLVII)

It appears that GDPM is the precursor of GDP-L-fucose in *Aerobacter aerogens*. The GDPM is first converted to GDP-4-keto-6-deoxy-D-mannose (XLVIII); this is isomerized and finally reduced by NADPH to GDP-L-fucose (XLIX) (177).

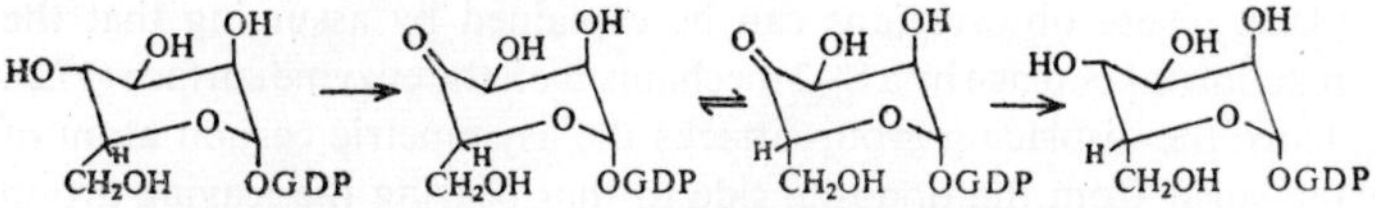

(XLVII)   (XLVIII)   (XLIX)

It is probable that guanosine diphosphate sugars are involved in polysaccharide biosynthesis in a manner which is yet unknown.

Adenosine diphosphate sugars. When the enzyme which catalyses the synthesis of starch from UDPG is treated with adenosine diphosphate-D-glucose (ADPG), the rate of reaction is increased approximately tenfold (178). ADPG and UDPG pyrophosphorylases can be separated chromatographically, which indicates that ADPG is not an artefact of UDPG. In addition, an enzyme has been found in wheat which will catalyse the biosynthesis of the enzyme from ATP and D-glucose-1 phosphate. ADP-glucose has been isolated from corn grains (179), and its structure proved in a manner analogous to that for UDPG.

Thymidine diphosphate sugars. A few thymidine diphosphate sugars, such as TDP-D-glucose (180), TDP-D-rhamnose (181) and TDP-D-mannose (181), have been isolated from bacteria. Their mode of biosynthesis appears to be by the usual method from the sugar phosphate and TTP.

$$\text{TTP} + \text{D-glucose-1 phosphate} \longrightarrow \text{TDP-D-glucose} + \text{PP}_i$$

The biological function of these coenzymes is unknown, but it is probable that they are involved in the biosynthesis of immunospecific capsular polysaccharides of bacteria.

Cytidine diphosphate coenzymes
(*a*) *Cytidine diphosphate choline and cytidine diphosphate ethanolamine.* The observation that crude ATP catalysed the incorporation of choline phosphate (L, R = CH$_3$) into lecithin in liver led to the discovery of a new class of coenzymes which were involved in the biosynthesis of lipids and fats (182). The crude ATP contained CTP, which reacted with cytidine phosphate to form cytidine diphosphate choline (LI, R = CH$_3$).

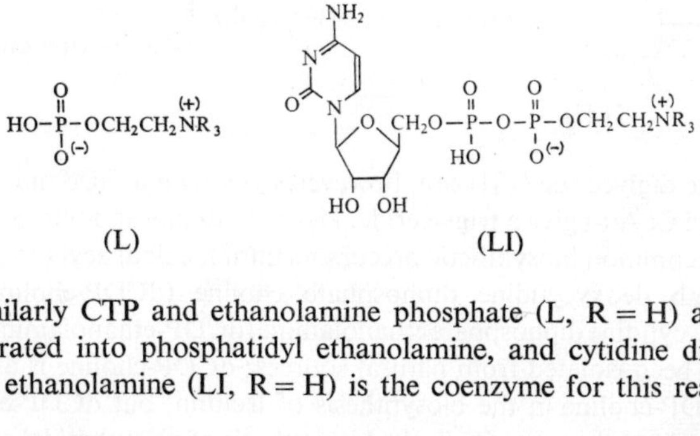

(L)   (LI)

Similarly CTP and ethanolamine phosphate (L, R = H) are incorporated into phosphatidyl ethanolamine, and cytidine diphosphate ethanolamine (LI, R = H) is the coenzyme for this reaction (183).

The two coenzymes have been synthesized by the carbodiimide route from CMP and the amino alcohol phosphate (184).

In the scheme for the biosynthesis of phospholipids, which has been put forward by Kennedy (185), the first stage is the phosphorylation of ATP to give L-glycerol-1 phosphate.

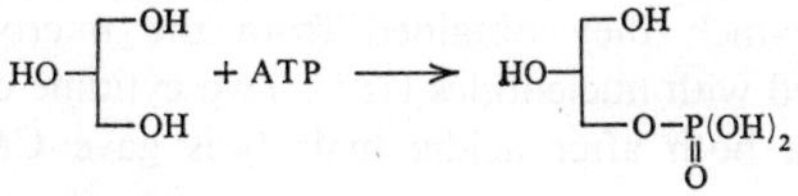

The latter then reacts with two molecules of S-acyl CoA to produce a diglyceride phosphate.

$$HO-\begin{bmatrix} OH \\ O-\overset{\underset{\|}{O}}{P}(OH)_2 \end{bmatrix} + 2\ CoASCOR \longrightarrow RCOO-\begin{bmatrix} OOCR \\ O-\overset{\underset{\|}{O}}{P}(OH)_2 \end{bmatrix}$$

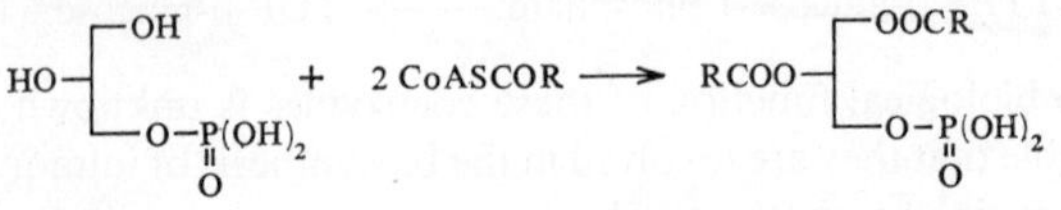

The phosphate group of the diglyceride phosphate is then removed by hydrolysis to give the free diglyceride (LII), which reacts with CDP-choline (or CDP-ethanolamine) to produce the phospholipid.

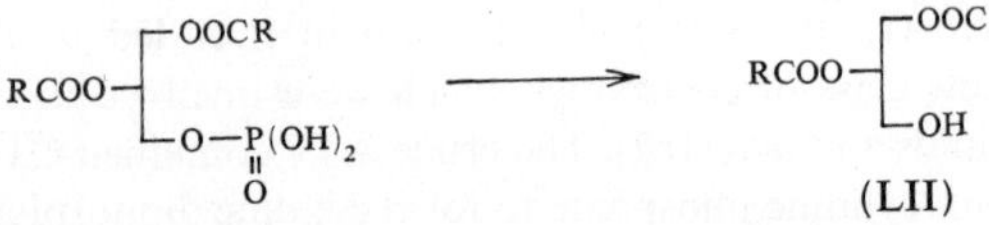

$$RCOO-\begin{bmatrix} OOCR \\ O-\overset{\underset{\|}{O}}{P}(OH)_2 \end{bmatrix} \longrightarrow RCOO-\begin{bmatrix} OOCR \\ OH \end{bmatrix}$$

(LII)

$$RCOO-\begin{bmatrix} OOCR \\ OH \end{bmatrix} + CDP-choline \longrightarrow RCOO-\begin{bmatrix} OOCR \\ O-\overset{\underset{\|}{O}}{\underset{O}{P}}-OCH_2CH_2N(CH_3)_3^{(+)} \end{bmatrix}$$

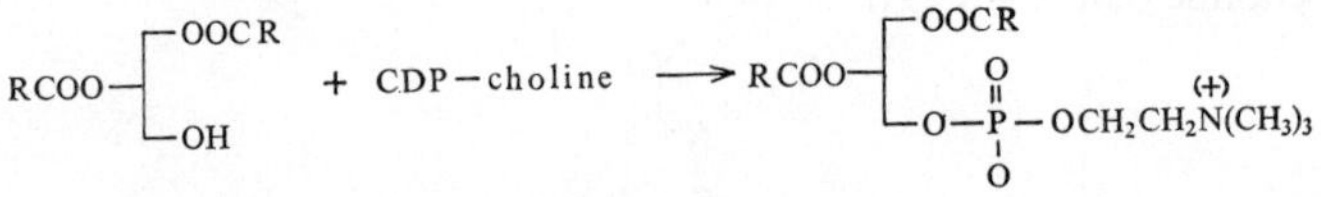

(LII)

The diglyceride (LII) can, however, react with a third molecule of S-acyl CoA to give a triglyceride. Hence both fats and phospholipids have common biosynthetic precursors until the final acylation step.

Both deoxycytidine diphosphate choline (dCDP-choline) and deoxycytidine diphosphate ethanolamine (dCDP-ethanolamine) (8, 9) have been isolated from natural sources; dCDP-choline is as active as CDP-choline in the biosynthesis of lecithin, but dCDP-ethanolamine has a low activity in the biosynthesis of phosphatidyl ethanolamine (186).

(b) *Cytidine diphosphate glycerol and cytidine diphosphate ribitol.* During their investigations on the phosphorylation of pantothenic acid in *Lactobacillus arabinosus* in connection with the biosynthesis of CoA, Baddiley and Mathias observed that the pantothenic acid phosphate which they obtained from the micro-organism was contaminated with nucleotides (187). Two cytidine derivatives were present, and both after acidic hydrolysis gave CMP. Treatment of these cytidine-containing compounds with rattlesnake (*Crotalus atrox*) venom gave cytidine, orthophosphate, and a single organic phosphate. *Crotalus atrox* venom contains both a pyrophosphatase and a 5′-nucleotidase, so the cytidine-containing compounds must be cytidine-5′ pyrophosphate esters. The organic phosphates were identified as L-glycerol-1 phosphate (187) and D-ribitol-5 phosphate (188). The two cytidine nucleotides must therefore be cytidine diphosphate glycerol and cytidine diphosphate ribitol respectively.

The configuration of the glycerol of CDP-glycerol was determined by its enzymic oxidation with NAD^+ and glycerophosphate dehydrogenase. This enzymic system is specific for L-glycerol-1 phosphate and hence the coenzyme must also be a derivative of L-glycerol. Hydrolysis of CDP-ribitol by hot ammonium hydroxide gave ribitol cyclic phosphate; this was then oxidized to glyceric acid-2,3 phosphate by an enzyme system from rabbit muscle which requires D-ribitol for activity (189).

Both CDP-glycerol and CDP-ribitol have been synthesized by the carbodiimide method (190, 191) from CMP and glycerol-1 or ribitol-5 phosphate. In each case the unesterified hydroxyl groups of the glycerol and ribitol phosphates were protected by isopropylidene groups to prevent the formation of cyclic phosphates.

CDP-glycerol and CDP-ribitol are synthesized enzymically from CTP and the appropriate alcohol phosphate in the usual way (192).

At the time of their discovery no obvious function could be assigned to the two cytidine nucleotides; however polymers, containing glycerol or ribitol phosphate were present in *Lactobacillus arabinosus* (193), and could be extracted from the bacteria with dilute acid. Baddiley therefore suggested, by analogy with the known properties of the uridine diphosphate sugars, that CDP-glycerol and CDP-ribitol were involved in the biosynthesis of these polymers. The glycerol- and ribitol-containing polymers were called teichoic acids and have been found in a wide variety of bacteria. In most of the teichoic acids, sugars are attached by glycosidic linkages, and D-alanine by ester linkages, to the polyhydric alcohols. Teichoic acids occur mainly in the cell walls of bacteria; however, a small amount of 'intracellular teichoic acid' which contains glycerol occurs within the bacterial cell (194).

Exhaustive extraction of bacterial cell walls with cold, dilute acid removes both the teichoic acids and soluble polysaccharides. The rigid residue is a mucopeptide, and it is thought that the teichoic acids are joined to the cell walls by both ionic and hydrogen bonds (195).

The structure of the teichoic acids from the cell walls of *Bacillus subtilis* has been established by both chemical and enzymic methods (195). The polymeric material consists of D-ribitol residues joined by phosphodiester linkages. The 4-hydroxyl group of the D-ribitol is joined to α-D-glucose by a glycosidic link and either the 2- or the 3-hydroxyl is esterified by a D-alanine moiety.

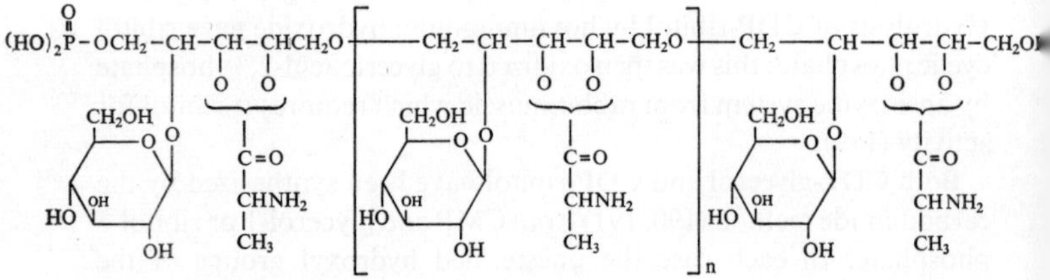

Other teichoic acids contain glycerol, and/or other sugars such as N-acetyl glucosamine (195).

Although the mechanism of the biosynthesis of teichoic acids is still unknown, Baddiley's original suggestion – that CDP-glycerol and CDP-ribitol play a part in this mechanism which is analogous to that played by UDPG in the biosynthesis of polysaccharides – is probably correct.

REFERENCES

1. FISKE and SUBBAROW (1929), *Science*, **70**, 381.
2. LOHMANN (1929), *Naturwiss.*, **17**, 624; (1935), *Biochem. Z.*, **282**, 120.
3. LYTHGOE and TODD (1945), *Nature*, **155**, 695.
4. BERGKVIST and DEUTSCH (1953), *Acta Chem. Scand.*, **7**, 1307.
5. BERGKVIST and DEUTSCH (1954), *Acta Chem. Scand.*, **8**, 1889.
6. POTTER, SCHLESINGER, BEUTTNER-JANUSCH, and THOMPSON (1957), *JBC*, **226**, 381.

7. LEHMANN, BESSMAN, SIMMS, and KORNBERG (1958), *JBC*, **233**, 163.

8. SUGINO (1957), *JACS*, **79**, 5074.

9. POTTER and BEUTTNER-JANUSCH (1958), *JBC*, **233**, 462.

10. BADDILEY and TODD (1947), *JCS*, 648.

11. BADDILEY, MICHELSON, and TODD (1949), *JCS*, 582.

12. KHORANA and TODD (1953), *JCS*, 2257.

13. KHORANA (1954), *JACS*, **76**, 3517.

14. KHORANA (1961), *Some recent developments in the chemistry of phosphate esters of biological interest*, Wiley, N.Y.

15. SMITH (1961), *Biochem. Preps.*, **8**, 1.

16. CLARK, KIRBY, and TODD (1957), *JCS*, 1497.

17. MOFFATT and KHORANA (1961), *JACS*, **83**, 649.

18. COHN and HUGHES (1962), *JBC*, **237**, 176.

19. MARRIAN (1954), *BBA*, **13**, 278.

20. SACKS (1955), *BBA*, **16**, 436.

21. LIEBERMAN (1955), *JACS*, **77**, 3373.

22. RACKER (1961), *Adv. in Enzymol.*, **23**, 323.

23. This subject is covered in detail in Volume 6 of *The Enzymes*.

24. GRUNBERG-MANAGO (1962), *Adv. in Biochem.*, **31**, 301.

25. GUNBERG-MANAGO and OCHOA (1955), *JACS*, **77**, 3165.

26. KORNBERG, LIEBERMAN, and SIMMS (1955), *JBC*, **215**, 389.

27. KELLER and ZAMECNIK (1956), *JBC*, **221**, 45.

28. NATHANS, VON EHRENSTEIN, MONRO, AND LIPMANN (1962), *Fed. Proc.*, **21**, 127.

29. HARDEN and YOUNG (1906), *Proc. Roy. Soc. B*, **78**, 369.

30. VON EULER, ALBERS, and SCHLENK (1936), *Z. physiol. Chem.*, **240**, 113.

31. WARBURG and CHRISTIAN (1936), *Biochem. Z.*, **287**, 291.

32. WARBURG and CHRISTIAN (1931), *Biochem Z.*, **242**, 206.

33. VON EULER, KARRER, and BECKER (1936), *Helv. Chim. Acta*, **19**, 1060.

34. VESTIN, SCHLENK, and VON EULER (1937), *Ber.*, **70**, 1369.

35. KARRER, SCHWARTZENBACH, BENZ, and SOLMSSEN (1936), *Helv. Chim. Acta*, **19**, 811.

36. KAPLAN, COLOWICK, and NASON (1951), *JBC*, **191**, 473.

37. HUGHES, KENNER, and TODD (1957), *JCS*, 3733.

38. HAYNES, HUGHES, KENNER, and TODD (1957), *JCS*, 3727.

39. FAWCETT and KAPLAN (1962), *JBC*, **237**, 1709.

40. VON EULER, ADLER, and ERIKSON (1937), *Z. physiol. Chem.*, **248**, 227.

41. VON EULER and ADLER (1938), *Z. physiol. Chem.*, **252**, 41.

42. VON EULER and SCHLENK, (1937), *Z. physiol. Chem.*, **246**, 64.
43. SCHLENK (1945), *Adv. in Enzymol.*, **5**, 207.
44. KORNBERG and PRICER (1950), *JBC*, **186**, 557.
45. PREISS and HANDLER (1958), *JBC*, **233**, 493.
46. FISCHER, CONN, VENNESLAND, and WESTHEIMER (1953), *JBC*, **202**, 687.
47. FISCHER, OFNER, CONN, VENNESLAND, and WESTHEIMER (1952), *Fed. Proc.*, **11**, 211.
48. PULLMAN and COLOWICK (1954), *JBC*, **206**, 121.
49. PULLMAN, SAN PIETRO, and COLOWICK (1954), *JBC*, **206**, 129.
50. WESTHEIMER and MAUZERALL (1955), *JACS*, **77**, 2261.
51. DUBB, SAUNDERS, and WANG (1958), *JACS*, **80**, 1767.
52. WESTHEIMER and HUTTON (1958), *Tetrahedron*, **3**, 73.
53. LEVY, TALALAY, and VENNESLAND (1962), *Prog. in Stereochem.*, **3**, 299.
54. CORNFORTH, RYBACK, POPJACK, DONNINGER, and SCHROEPFER, (1962), *Biochem. Biophys. Res. Commun.*, **9**, 371.
55. SIEGEL, MONTGOMERY, and BOCK (1959), *Arch. Biochem. Biophys.*, **82**, 288.
56. LEMIEUX and LOWN (1963), *Canad. J. Chem.*, **41**, 889.
57. KAPLAN (1960), *The Enzymes*, **3**, 148.
58. BOYER and THEORELL (1956), *Acta Chem. Scand.*, **10**, 447.
59. WILLIAMS, HOCH, and VALLEE (1958), *JBC*, **232**, 465.
60. DUYSENS and KRONENBERG (1957), *BBA*, **26**, 437.
61. KAPLAN, CIOTTI, and STOLTZENBACH (1956), *JBC*, **221**, 833.
62. RODKEY and DONOVAN (1959), *JBC*, **234**, 677.
63. WALLENFELS and SCHÜLY (1959), *Annalen*, **621**, 86.
64. WALLENFELS (1959), *Steric Course of Microbiological Reactions*, Churchill. London, p. 18.
65. WALLENFELS and GELLRICH (1959), *Annalen*, **621**, 198.
66. COMMONER, LIPPINCOTT, and PASSONEAU (1958), *PNAS*, **44**, 1099.
67. DIXON and WEBB (1958), *Enzymes*, Longmans, London.
68. MERRIT and TOMKINS (1959), *JBC*, **234**, 2778.
69. NIELANDS (1952), *JBC*, **199**, 373.
70. BURTON and WILSON (1953), *BJ*, **54**, 86.
71. BARANOWSKI (1949), *JBC*, **180**, 535.
72. SEEGMILLER (1953), *JBC*, **201**, 629.
73. KING and CHELDELIN (1956), *JBC*, **220**, 177.
74. GLASER and BROWN (1955), *JBC*, **216**, 67.
75. BRINK (1953), *Acta Chem. Scand.*, **7**, 1081.
76. LEHNINGER and WADKINS (1962), *Ann. Rev. Biochem.*, **31**, 47.

77. BARLTROP, GRUBB, and HESP (1963), *Nature*, **199**, 759.
78. GRIFFITHS (1963), *Fed. Proc.*, **22**, 1064.
79. KUHN, RUDY, and WEYGAND (1935), *Ber.*, **68**, 625.
80. KUHN and RUDY (1934), *Ber.*, **67**, 1826.
81. KUHN, RUDY, and WAGNER-JAUREGG (1933), *Ber.*, **66**, 1950.
82. KARRER, SALOMON, SCHÖPP, SCHLITTLER, and FRITZSCHE (1934), *Helv. Chim. Acta*, **17**, 1010.
83. KUHN (1936), *Angew.*, **49**, 6.
84. WARBURG and CHRISTIAN (1932), *Naturwiss.*, **20**, 688.
85. THEORELL (1935), *Biochem. Z.*, **278**, 263.
86. KUHN, RUDY, and WEYGAND (1936), *Ber*, **69**, 1543.
87. KARRER, FREI, and MEERWEIN (1937), *Helv. Chim. Acta*, **20**, 79.
88. WARBURG and CHRISTIAN (1938), *Biochem. Z.*, **298**, 150.
89. ABRAHAM (1939), *BJ*, **33**, 543.
90. CHRISTIE, KENNER, and TODD (1954), *JCS*, 46.
91. HEUNNEKENS and KILGOUR (1955), *JACS*, **77**, 6716.
92. DELUCA and KAPLAN (1956), *JBC*, **223**, 569.
93. KHORANA and MOFFATT (1958), *JACS*, **80**, 3756.
94. PLAUT (1961), *Ann Rev. Biochem.*, **30**, 409.
95. MCNUTT (1956), *JBC*, **219**, 365.
96. MCNUTT (1954), *JBC*, **210**, 511.
97. MASUDA (1955), *Pharm. Bull. (Tokyo)*, **3**, 434.
98. ROWAN and WOOD (1963), *Proc. Chem. Soc.*, 21.
99. PLAUT (1963), *JBC*, **238**, 2225.
100. ENGLARD (1953), *JACS*, **75**, 6048.
101. SCHRECKER and KORNBERG (1950), *JBC*, **182**, 795.
102. LOWE and CLARKE (1956), *JBC*, **221**, 983.
103. PALMER, BRAY, and BEINERT (1963), *Fed. Proc.*, **22**, 466.
104. MAHLER (1956), *Adv. in Enzymol.*, **17**, 233.
105. HAAS, HORECKER, and HOGNESS (1940), *JBC*, **136**, 747.
106. HORECKER (1950), *JBC*, **183**, 593.
107. MAHLER, SARKAR, VERNON, and ALBERTY (1952), *JBC*, **199**, 585.
108. MEROLA, COLEMAN, and HANSEN (1963), *Fed. Proc.*, **22**, 466.
109. WELLNER and MEISTER (1961), *JBC*, **236**, 2357.
110. MACKLER, MAHLER, and GREEN (1954), *JBC*, **210**, 149.
111. DE RENZO (1956), *Adv. in Enzymol.*, **17**, 293.
112. NASON and EVANS (1953), *JBC*, **202**, 655.
113. LAZZARINI and ATKINSON (1961), *JBC*, **236**, 3330.
114. HUENNEKENS, FELTON, RAO, and MACKLER (1961), *JBC*, **236**, PC57.
115. VEEGER (1964), *14th Mosbacher Colloq.*, Springer Verlag, Berlin.

116. LINDBERG, GRABE, LÖW, SIEKEVITZ, and ERNSTER (1958), *Acta Chem. Scand.*, **12**, 598.

117. LIPMANN (1945), *JBC*, **160**, 173.

118. KAPLAN and LIPMANN (1948), *JBC*, **174**, 37.

119. STADTMAN, DOUDOROFF, and LIPMANN (1951), *JBC*, **191**, 377.

120. BADDILEY (1955), *Adv. in Enzymol.*, **16**, 1.

121. LIPMANN (1953), *Bacteriol. Rev.*, **17**, 1.

122. SNELL and BROWN (1953), *Adv. in Enzymol.*, **14**, 49.

123. KHORANA and MOFFATT (1961), *JACS*, **83**, 663.

124. MICHELSON (1961), *BBA*, **50**, 605.

125. GRUBER and LYNEN (1962), *Annalen*, **659**, 139.

126. LIPMANN, KAPLAN, NOVELLI, TUTTLE, and GUIRARD (1947), *JBC*, **167**, 869.

127. DEVRIES, EVANS, GOVIER, GREGORY, NOVELLI, SOODAK, and LIPMANN (1950), *JACS*, **72** 4838.

128. WILLIAMS (1943), *Adv. in Enzymol.*, **3**, 253.

129. BROWN, CRAIG, and SNELL (1950), *Arch. Biochem. Biophys.*, **27**, 473.

130. BROWN and SNELL (1953), *JACS*, **75**, 1691.

131. GREGORY and LIPMANN (1952), *JACS*, **74**, 4017.

132. BADDILEY and THAIN (1952), *JCS*, 800.

133. GREGORY, NOVELLI, and LIPMANN (1952), *JACS*, **74**, 854.

134. WANG, SHUSTER, and KAPLAN (1952), *JACS*, **74**, 3204.

135. WANG, SHUSTER, and KAPLAN (1954), *JBC*, **206**, 299.

136. NOVELLI, FLYNN, and LIPMANN (1949), *JBC*, **177**, 493.

137. BADDILEY and THAIN (1951), *JCS*, 3421.

138. BROWN and REYNOLDS (1963), *Ann. Rev. Biochem.*, **32**, 419.

139. SIMON and SHEMIN (1953), *JACS*, **75**, 2520.

140. LYNEN, REICHERT, and RUEFF (1951), *Annalen*, **574**, 1.

141. CHOU and LIPMANN (1952), *JBC*, **196**, 89.

142. KORNBERG and PRICER (1954), *JBC*, **204**, 345.

143. STADTMAN (1952), *Fed. Proc.*, **11**, 291.

144. STADTMAN (1952), *JBC*, **196**, 527.

145. BRADY and KOVAL (1958), *JBC*, **233**, 26.

146. WAITE and WAKIL (1963), *JBC*, **238**, 81.

147. ALLEN, STJERNHOLM, and WOOD (1963), *JBC*, **238**, PC2890.

148. KNAPPE, RINGELMANN, and LYNEN (1961), *Biochem Z.*, **335**, 168.

149. KNAPPE, WENGER, and WIELAND (1963), *Biochem. Z.*, **337**, 232.

150. LANE AND LYNEN (1963), *PNAS*, **49**, 1379.

151. WOOD, LOCHMÜLLER, RIEPERTINGER, and LYNEN (1963), *Biochem. Z.*, **337**, 247.

152. BRADY, BRADLEY, and TRAMS (1960), *JBC*, **235**, 3093.
153. BRESSLER and WAKIL (1961), *JBC*, **236**, 643.
154. MAHLER (1953), *Fed. Proc.*, **12**, 694.
155. CAPUTTO, LELOIR, CARDINI, and PALDINI (1950), *JBC*, **184**, 333.
156. PALDINI and LELOIR (1952), *BJ*, **51**, 426.
157. KHORANA, TENER, WRIGHT, and MOFFATT (1957), *JACS*, **79**, 430.
158. KENNER, TODD, and WEBB (1954), *JCS*, 2843.
159. MICHELSON and TODD (1956), *JCS*, 3459.
160. TRUCCO (1951), *Arch. Biochem. Biophys.*, **34**, 482.
161. NEUFELD, GINSBURG, PUTMAN, FANSHIER, and HASSID (1957), *Arch. Biochem. Biophys.*, **69**, 602.
162. HASSID, NEUFELD, and FEINGOLD (1959), *PNAS*, **45**, 905.
163. KALCKAR and MAXWELL (1956), *BBA*, **22**, 588.
164. LELOIR and CARDINI (1955), *JBC*, **214**, 157.
165. BEAN and HASSID (1955), *JACS*, **77**, 5737.
166. GANDER, PETERSEN, AND BOYER (1957), *Arch. Biochem. Biophys.*, **69**, 85.
167. DUTTON and STOREY (1954), *BJ*, **57**, 275.
168. SMITH, MILLS, and HARPER (1957), *BBA*, **23**, 662.
169. LELOIR, and CARDINI (1957), *JBC*, **225**, 317.
170. GINSBURG, STUMPF, and HASSID (1956), *JBC*, **223**, 977.
171. MARKOVITZ, CIFONELLI, and DORFMAN (1959), *JBC*, **234**, 2343.
172. KOSHLAND (1959), *The Enzymes*, **1**, 305.
173. CABIB and LELOIR (1954), *JBC*, **206**, 779.
174. MUNCH-PETERSEN (1955), *Arch. Biochem. Biophys.*, **55**, 592.
175. PONTIS, JAMES, and BADDILEY (1960), *BJ*, **75**, 428.
176. GINSBURG (1960), *JBC*, **235**, 2196.
177. GINSBURG (1961), *JBC*, **236**, 2389.
178. ESPADA (1962), *JBC*, **237**, 3577.
179. RECONDO, DANKERT, and LELOIR (1963), *Biochem. Biophys. Res. Commun.*, **12**, 204.
180. KORNFELD and GLASER (1961), *JBC*, **236**, 1791.
181. BLUMSON and BADDILEY (1961), *BJ*, **81**, 114.
182. KENNEDY and WEISS (1955), *JACS*, **77**, 250.
183. KENNEDY and WEISS (1956), *JBC*, **222**, 193.
184. KENNEDY and WEISS (1956), *JBC*, **222**, 185.
185. KENNEDY (1957), *Ann. Rev. Biochem.*, **26**, 119.
186. KENNEDY, BORKENHAGEN, and SMITH (1959), *JBC*, **234**, 1998.
187. BADDILEY, BUCHANAN, MATHAIS, and SANDERSON (1956), *JCS*, 4186.
188. BADDILEY, BUCHANAN, CARSS, and MATHIAS (1956), *JCS*, 4583.

189. BADDILEY, BUCHANAN, and CARSS (1957), *JCS*, 1869.

190. BADDILEY, BUCHANAN, and SANDERSON (1958), *JCS*, 3107.

191. BADDILEY, BUCHANAN, and FAWCETT (1959), *JCS*, 2192.

192. SHAW (1962), *BJ*, **82**, 297.

193. ARMSTRONG, BADDILEY, BUCHANAN, CARSS, and GREENBERG (1958), *JCS*, 4344.

194. BADDILEY and DAVISON (1961), *J. gen. Microbiol.*, **24**, 295.

195. BADDILEY, *J. Royal Inst. Chem.* (1962), **86**, 366.

CHAPTER FOUR

Pyridoxal Phosphate and Thiamine Pyrophosphate

4.1 Introduction

In the previous chapter the coenzymes have all contained a nucleotidic portion which was not directly involved in the biochemical processes which were catalysed by the coenzyme. In this chapter, two non-nucleotidic coenzymes, pyridoxal phosphate and thiamine pyrophosphate, are discussed. The main function of the phosphate and the pyrophosphate groups in pyridoxal phosphate and thiamine pyrophosphate respectively is to bind the coenzyme to a specific site on the apoenzyme, in order that the rest of the molecule is in position to react with a substrate.

The reactive centre in pyridoxal phosphate is the aldehyde group which interacts with amino compounds to form Schiff bases (imines). These Schiff bases can then (*a*) undergo hydrolysis to give the deaminated product; (*b*) decompose to give the racemic amino compound; or (*c*) eliminate groups from the parent amino compound. These reactions are particularly important in the case of amino acids, and pyridoxal plays a vital role in the metabolism of amino acids (*vide infra*).

The reactive centre in thiamine pyrophosphate is the thiazolium ring, which can produce carbanions in a stabilized form, and thiamine pyrophosphate is the cofactor for a number of reactions in which carbanions are intermediates, for example, acyloin condensations and the decarboxylation of α-keto acids.

4.2 Pyridoxal phosphate

Discovery and Structural elucidation of pyridoxine. Vitamin B_6, an antipellagra factor, was isolated in 1934 from yeast, rice bran, and liver by György (1) who found it to be a nitrogen-containing base which could form a hydrochloride. The structure of Vitamin B_6, or pyridoxine (1), was elucidated by Kuhn and his co-workers a few years later (2–5).

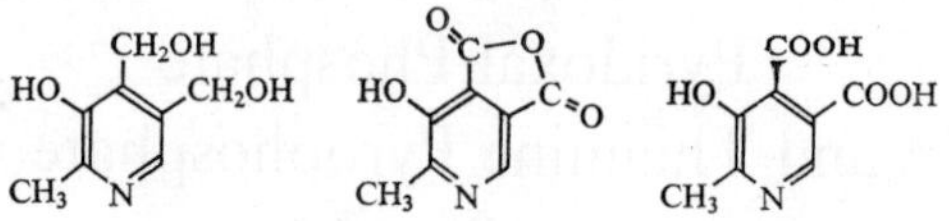

The main steps in the structural proof of pyridoxine were the following:

(i) Only one of the hydroxyl groups could be methylated by diazomethane, thus two of the hydroxyls were alcoholic and one was phenolic.

(ii) Monomethyl pyridoxine was unaffected by lead tetra-acetate, so the two alcoholic hydroxyls were not on adjacent carbon atoms.

(iii) Monomethyl pyridoxine was oxidized by cold permanganate to a monocarboxylic acid which could readily form a lactone.

(iv) Pyridoxine and 3-hydroxy pyridine had a very similar ultra-violet spectra.

(v) Monomethyl pyridoxine was oxidized with hot permanganate to a tricarboxylic acid which had the properties of a pyridine-1 carboxylic acid. When the tricarboxylic acid was heated, the molecule lost a molecule of water and a molecule of carbon dioxide. The resulting anhydride could then be hydrolysed to a dibasic acid which did not have the properties of a pyridine-1 carboxylic acid.

From the evidence quoted above, Kuhn put forward the structure (II) for the anhydride, and subsequent synthetic work proved this structure to be correct. Careful oxidation of monomethyl pyridoxine gave a dibasic acid (III) with an intact methyl group. This dibasic acid did not have the properties of a pyridine-1 carboxylic acid. Kuhn then put forward the structure (I) for pyridoxine and this was later confirmed independently by Stiller, Keresztesy, and Stevens (6). The latter authors provided the additional evidence of the presence of a phenol with an unsubstituted para position, as the vitamin gave a blue colour with 2,6-dichloro quinonechlorimide.

Kuhn's synthesis of pyridoxine started from the synthetic dibasic acid (III) and his route is outlined below (7).

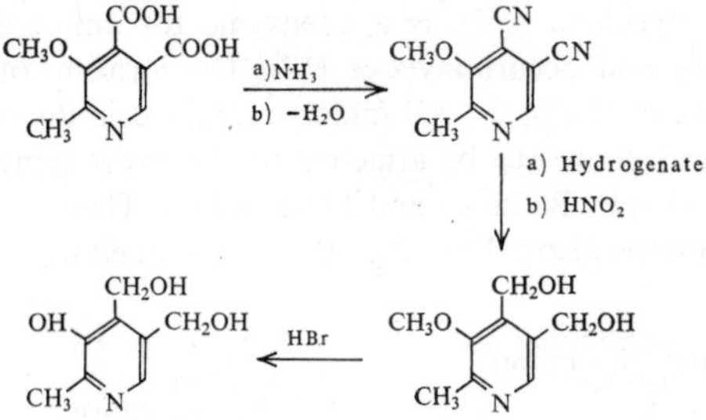

Discovery and structural elucidation of pyridoxal and pyridoxamine. The initial discovery that lactic acid bacteria require pyridoxine as a growth factor (8) led to the development of a biological method of assay for pyridoxine (9). However, anomalous results were soon obtained, and the existence of a compound with a much higher biological activity than pyridoxine was proposed (10). The activity of pyridoxine is increased after heating in an autoclave, especially in the presence of ammonia (11); the increased activity was due to the aldehyde pyridoxal (IV) and the amine pyridoxamine (V). These compounds were synthesized by Folkers and his co-workers (12).

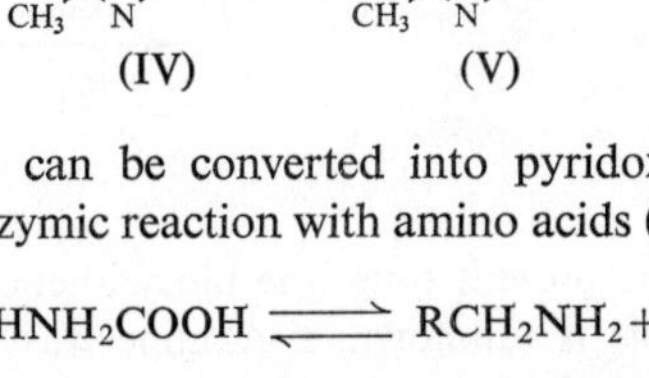

Pyridoxal (IV) can be converted into pyridoxamine (V) by a reversible non-enzymic reaction with amino acids (13).

$$RCHO + R'CHNH_2COOH \rightleftharpoons RCH_2NH_2 + R'CO COOH$$

Discovery and structure of pyridoxal phosphate. When ATP and pyridoxal were added to tissues from Vitamin B_6 deficient rats, their transaminating activity was partially restored *in vitro* (14). This activation of pyridoxal by ATP led to the theory that a pyridoxal phosphate was a coenzyme for transamination reactions *in vivo*. Pyridoxal phosphate, prepared by the action of phosphorus oxychloride on pyridoxal (15), is a coenzyme for amino acid transaminases (16) and decarboxylases (17). The location of the phosphoryl residue on the pyridoxal moiety remained in doubt for some years, and was shown to be attached to the hydroxymethyl group of pyridoxal (VI) by Baddiley and Mathais (18). Their unambiguous synthesis from the alcohol pyridoxol* (I) is outlined below.

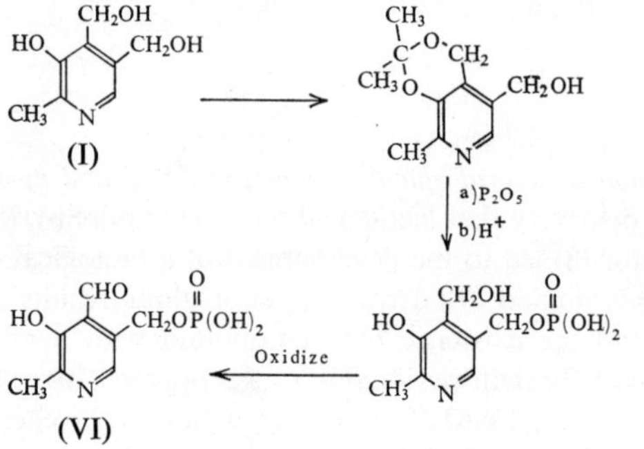

Pyridoxamine phosphate can be prepared either by direct phosphorylation of pyridoxamine (V), or by catalytic hydrogenation of the oxime of pyridoxal phosphate (VI) (19, 20, 21).

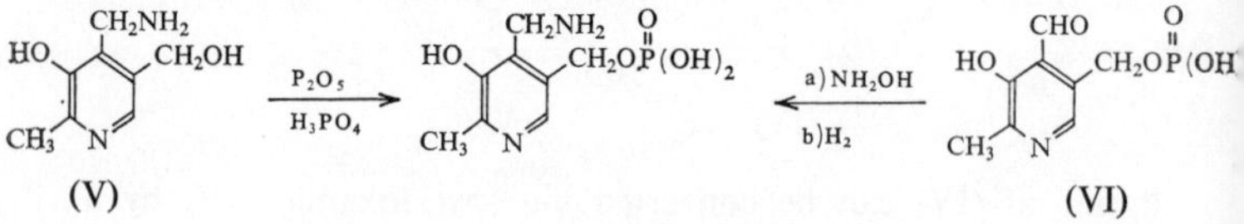

Biosynthesis. At the present time, the biosynthetic pathway to the pyridoxine molecule is unknown. D-Alanine was thought to be a precursor as it will replace the vitamin in growth media for *Strepto-*

---

*The alcohol of the vitamin B_6 group is called pyridoxol; the aldehyde, pyridoxal; and the amine, pyridoxamine. The name pyridoxine will be applied to the whole group of B_6 vitamins when the exact constitution is not stated.

coccus faecalis and *Lactobacillus casei*; however, this has since been disproved (22). A pyridoxol oxidase has been discovered which will convert the alcohol to the aldehyde, but it is not certain whether this is a biosynthetic reaction (23).

A kinase which will catalyse the phosphorylation of pyridoxal, pyridoxamine, and pyridoxol by ATP has been isolated from brewer's yeast and also occurs in brain, liver, *E. Coli*, and *S. faecalis* (24).

$$\text{Pyridoxal} + \text{ATP} \rightleftharpoons \text{Pyridoxal phosphate} + \text{ADP}$$

A model for the biochemical function of pyridoxal phosphate. Pyridoxal phosphate can catalyse three enzymic reactions of amino acids: (i) the activation of a hydrogen atom α to the amino group – this includes transamination and racemization reactions, (ii) the elimination of carbon dioxide, (iii) elimination of other groups from the amino acid (25).

The first stage in all these reactions is the formation of an imine (Schiff base) between the aldehyde group of pyridoxal and the amino group of the substrate.

$$\text{RCHO} + \text{R}'\text{NH}_2 \rightleftharpoons \text{RCH}{=}\text{NR}' + \text{H}_2\text{O}$$

The imines formed from pyridoxal phosphate and amino acids will form at least two types of stable metal chelates, those containing one pyridoxal molecule per metal atom (VII) and those with two pyridoxal molecules per metal atom (VIII) (27).

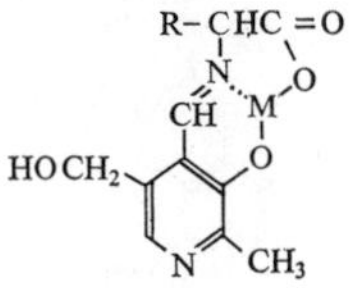

(VII) 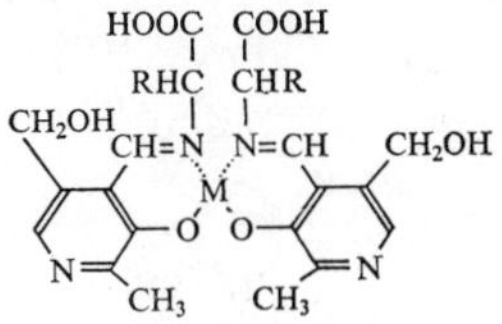   (VIII)

The rapid, metal-ion catalysed, non-enzymic transamination reaction between pyridoxal and amino acids is evidence for the participation of such chelates in enzymic transaminations which are catalysed by pyridoxal phosphate (28).

Structural features which must be present in the pyridoxine molecule for activity in the non-enzymic transamination reaction are (i) both a free phenolic hydroxyl in the 3-position and a formyl group in the 4-position, (ii) the ring nitrogen atom as salicylaldehyde is inactive. This must be due to the electron withdrawing power of the nitrogen atom as both 4- and 6-nitro salicylaldehyde are active. Neither the 2-methyl nor the 5-hydroxymethyl groups are required for the non-enzymic reaction, as analogues of pyridoxal phosphate with these two groups replaced are still active. The 2-methyl group is required for full enzymic activity, as is the phosphoryl residue on the 5-hydroxy methyl group. The function of these last two groups is probably to orientate the pyridoxal molecule correctly on the surface of the apoenzyme.

A scheme for the non enzymic transamination and racemization reaction involving metal chelates of pyridoxal has been put forward by Snell and his co-workers (29).

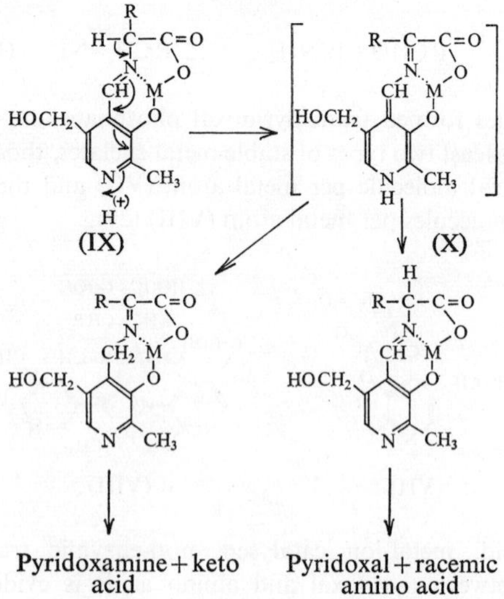

Pyridoxamine + keto acid   Pyridoxal + racemic amino acid

The azomethine (X) is a common intermediate for both the transamination and the racemization reactions. The tautomeric azomethine (IX) can also be an intermediate for elimination of carbon dioxide from the amino acid,

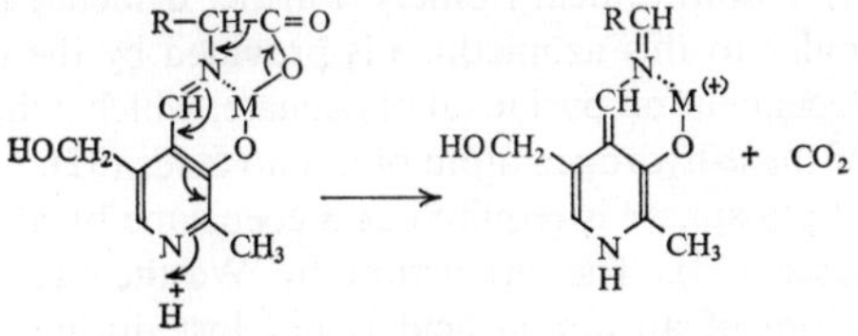

(IX)

and the elimination of a group β to the amino group.

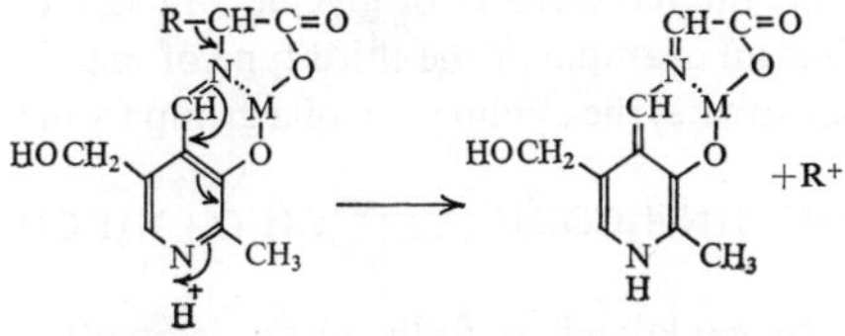

(IX)

$\alpha\beta$-Elimination reactions of amino acids, for example the reaction of pyridoxal with serine (30), can also be explained by a similar mechanism.

$$HOCH_2\underset{\underset{NH_2}{|}}{CH}\,COOH \xrightarrow[M^{II}]{\text{pyridoxal}} CH_3COCOOH + NH_3$$

Elimination of a group γ to the imine nitrogen in the azomethine (X) can take place as follows:

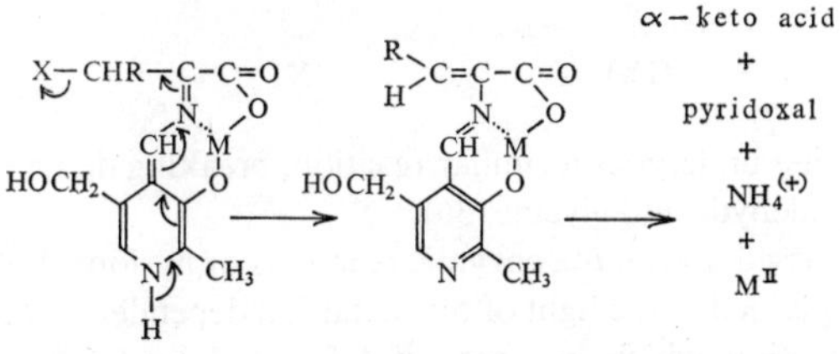

(X)

7

The reactions of pyridoxal phosphate in vivo. Numerous enzymes are known which catalyse the transamination and racemization reactions of amino acids (31). The α-carbon atom of the amino acid loses its asymmetry in the azomethine (IX) and replacement of the hydrogen atom will give both optical isomers. Further evidence for an intermediate similar to this azomethine is provided by the discovery of enzymes, dependent on pyridoxal phosphate, which will catalyse the exchange of the α-hydrogen atom of amino acids (32).

Pyridoxal phosphate is required as a coenzyme by all amino acid decarboxylases (33). The prediction by Westheimer that the α-hydrogen atom of an amino acid is not lost during enzymic decarboxylation is in accord with the mechanism outlined above, and has been verified experimentally (34).

The enzymic interconversion of glycine and serine in pigeon liver extracts (35) is an example of the third type of reaction catalysed by pyridoxal phosphate, the elimination of a group from the amino acid.

$$CH_2OHCHNH_2COOH \rightleftharpoons CH_2O + NH_2CH_2COOH$$

This can be explained as follows: the azomethine (IX, $R = H$) can eliminate formaldehyde to give the imine of glycine (X, $R = H$). This reaction is reversible and the imine (X) can add on formaldehyde to give (IX, $R = H$)

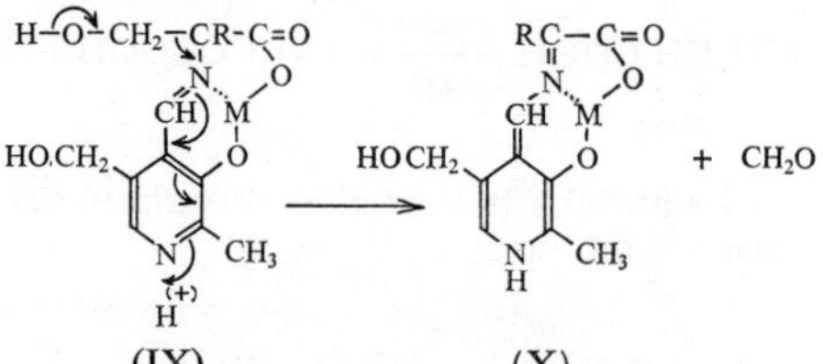

(IX)   (X)

Threonine undergoes a similar reaction, breaking down reversibly into acetaldehyde and glycine (36).

As discussed above, the enzymic reactions of pyridoxal phosphate can be explained in the light of the metal-ion dependent non-enzymic model reaction which has been put forward by Snell. However, highly purified pyridoxal phosphate enzymes do not appear to require metal ions for their activity (37). The apoenzyme must fulfil the function of the metal ion, and it is of interest that imidazole will catalyse the transamination of pyridoxal by α-amino phenylacetic acid *in vitro* (38). It is possible that a histidine residue in the apoenzyme can function as the complexing agent required by the model reaction scheme.

The apoenzymes of all pyridoxine dependent enzymes, except transaminases, have a specific requirement for pyridoxal phosphate as coenzyme. Transaminases, however, can be activated by pyridoxamine phosphate as well as pyridoxal phosphate (39). This is in accord with the model reaction scheme as a transaminase should exist in two forms, one capable of interacting with ketoacids (the pyridoxamine form), and the other capable of interacting with amino acids (the pyridoxal form).

The high activity of pyridoxamine phosphate as a growth factor for lactic acid bacteria indicates that this compound has a biochemical function which has yet to be elucidated (40).

4.3 Thiamine Pyrophosphate

Discovery and structural elucidation of thiamine. The tropical disease beriberi can be prevented by a diet containing unmilled rice and other unprocessed cereals. Vitamin B_1, or thiamine, the active factor, was first isolated from an acid extract of rice as the crystalline hydrochloride by Jansen and Donath,* who unfortunately overlooked the presence of sulphur in the vitamin (41). This omission was corrected by Windaus, who put forward the empirical formula of the hydrochloride as $C_{12}H_{18}Cl_2N_4OS$ (42). Windaus was able to cleave thiamine under oxidative conditions into two unidentified fragments.

The most significant, and fruitful, degradation of thiamine was performed by Williams who was able to split the vitamin into an acidic and a basic fragment (both containing sulphur) by the action of aqueous sodium sulphite (43). The acid fragment was a

* The isolation of crystalline vitamin B_1 by Jansen and Donath in 1926 was an important landmark in biochemistry, as this was the first time a vitamin had been obtained in a crystalline form.

pyrimidine sulphonic acid, and from a comparison of the ultraviolet spectrum of the sulphonic acid with spectra of pyrimidines of known structure, Williams suggested that the compound was 4-amino 6-ethyl pyrimidine-5 sulphonic acid (XI). The basic fragment was a thiazole which could be oxidized to 4-methyl thiazole-5 carboxylic acid (XII, R = COOH). This was the same acid as the sulphur-containing compound which Windaus had isolated from the oxidative cleavage of thiamine (42). Williams concluded that the basic fragment was 4-methyl 5-β-hydroxyethyl thiazole (XII, R = CH$_2$CH$_2$OH) and that the vitamin had the formula (XIII).

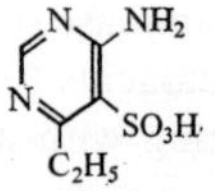

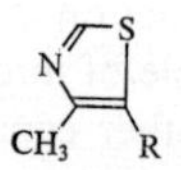

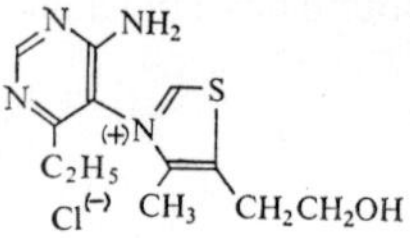

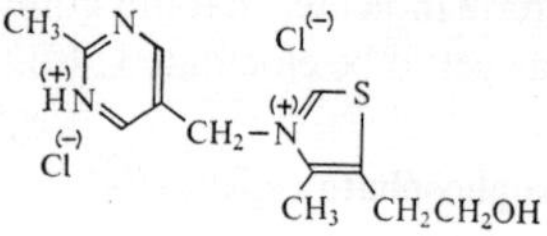

The thiazole (XII, R = CH$_2$CH$_2$OH) was synthesized by Clarke and Gurin (44) as follows:

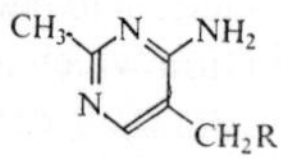

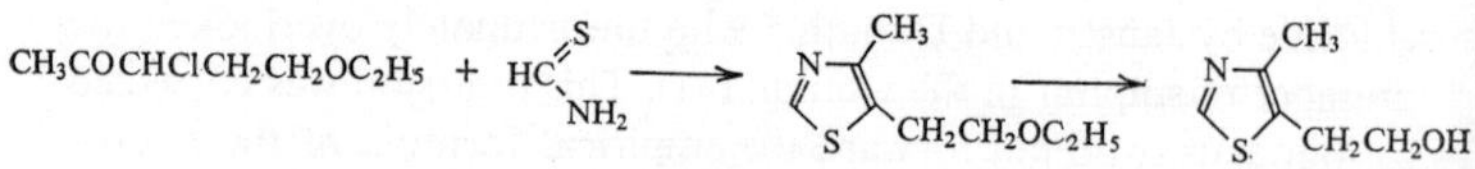

After he had isolated 2,5-dimethyl 4-amino pyrimidine (XV) from the reduction with sodium and liquid ammonia of the pyrimidine sulphonic acid, Williams corrected his original proposal for the structure of Vitamin B$_1$ hydrochloride to (XIV) (45).

The vitamin was synthesized independently, and practically simultaneously, by Williams (46) and Andersag and Westphal (47). These two syntheses have a common last stage, the coupling of the

5-halogenomethyl pyrimidine (XV, R = Hal.) with the thiazole (XII, R = CH_2CH_2OH).

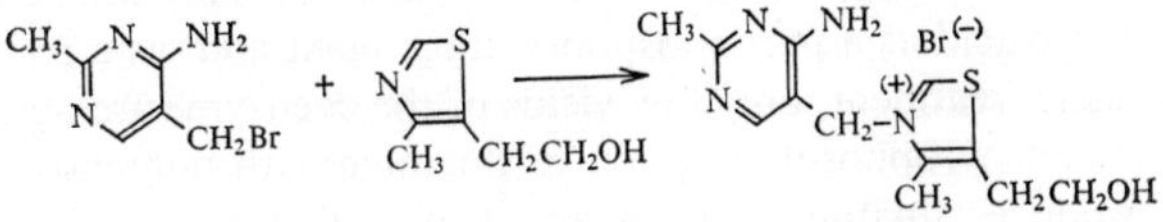

(XIV)

Todd and Bergel (48), however, built up the thiazolium ring *in situ* as their final stage.

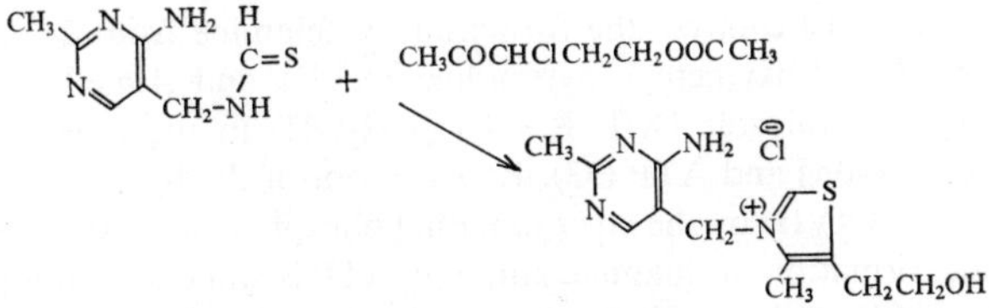

Structural elucidation of thiamine pyrophosphate (*cocarboxylase*). The coenzyme of yeast carboxylase, an enzyme system which will catalyse the decarboxylation of α-keto acids, was isolated by Lohmann and Schuster soon after the final structural assignment of thiamine was published (49). The coenzyme contained two atoms of phosphorus per molecule and could be hydrolysed by acid to the inactive mono-phosphate. Enzymic hydrolysis of the coenzyme gave thiamine, so the main structural problem was the position of attachment of the pyrophosphoryl moiety. There is only one position in the thiamine molecule which would give a stable derivative of pyrophosphoric acid, and that is the β-hydroxyethyl moiety on the thiazolium ring. The structure of thiamine pyrophosphate must be (XVI) and this has been confirmed by synthesis. Thiamine pyrophosphate has been shown to

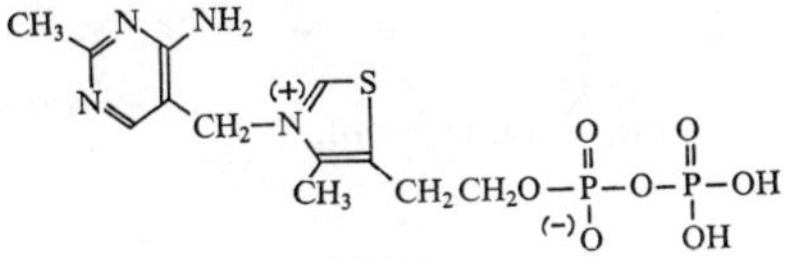

(XVI)

possess a high activity as a catalyst for decarboxylation reactions in brain tissue (50).

The synthetic approaches to cocarboxylase normally utilize polyphosphoric acid as a pyrophosphorylating agent and, as a result of this drastic treatment, only low yields of the coenzyme are obtained (51). Direct pyrophosphorylation of thiamine with polyphosphoric acid produces thiamine mono- and triphosphates as well as the desired diphosphate. Both the mono- and triphosphates have been isolated from natural sources, but no catalytic activity in enzymic systems has been reported so far (52).

Biosynthesis of thiamine and thiamine pyrophosphate. Cell-free extracts of yeast catalyse the formation of thiamine from 2-methyl 4-amino 6-hydroxymethyl pyrimidine (XVII) and 4-methyl 5-β-hydroxyethyl thiazole (XII, R = CH_2CH_2OH) in the presence of magnesium ions and ATP (53). Replacement of the hydroxymethyl pyrimidine (XVII) by the corresponding phosphate (XVIII) accelerates the formation of thiamine although ATP is still essential for the reaction (54). Thiamine is synthesized by the cell-free yeast extracts in the absence of ATP if the pyrimidine pyrophosphate (XIX) and the thiazole phosphate (XII, R = $CH_2CH_2OPO_3H_2$) are substrates (55).

The pyrimidine pyrophosphate (XIX) is formed by two successive steps by the action of ATP on the hydroxymethyl pyrimidine (XVIII).

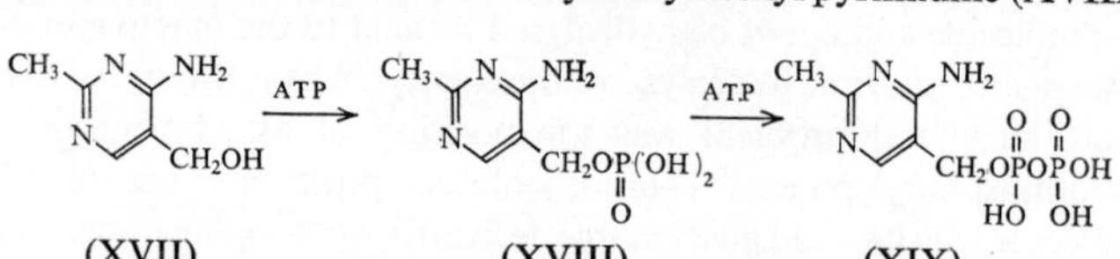

(XVII)   (XVIII)   (XIX)

The pyrimidine pyrophosphate then reacts with the thiazole phosphate to produce thiamine mono-phosphate (XX).

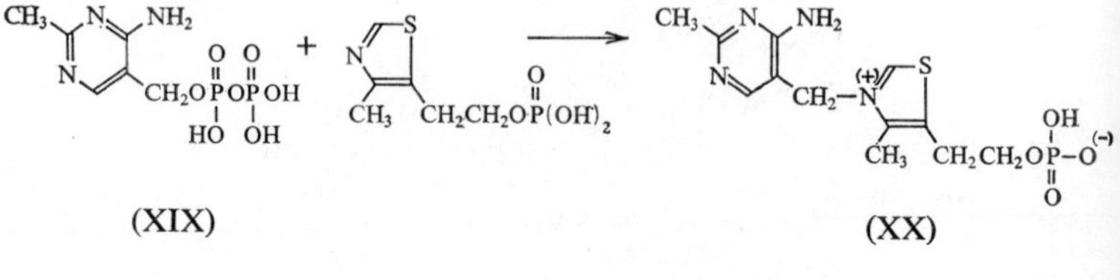

(XIX)   (XX)

Thiamine monophosphate is not phosphorylated directly to the diphosphate in yeast, but is first hydrolysed to free thiamine which is then pyrophosphorylated by ATP to the coenzyme (57)

Thiamine monophosphate $\longrightarrow$ Thiamine + P_i

Thiamine + ATP $\longrightarrow$ Thiamine pyrophosphate + AMP

Chemical properties of thiamine. There are two reactive centres in thiamine and these are the bridge methylene group and C_2 in the thiazolium ring.

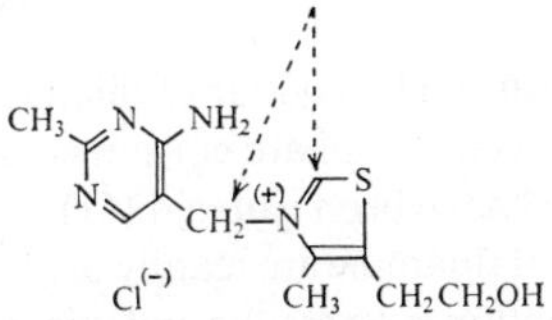

The active centres of thiamine

The displacement of a benzyl group from quaternary benzyl-ammonium salts following nucleophilic attack on the nitrogen atom is a common reaction of this type of compound, and nucleophiles such as sulphide and cyanate are powerful enough to carry out this displacement (57).

The proton which is attached to the C_2 carbon atom in the thiazolium ring of thiamine is labile owing to the proximity of the quaternary nitrogen atom. This lability is emphasized by the rapid, base-catalyzed exchange of this proton with deuterium oxide (58).

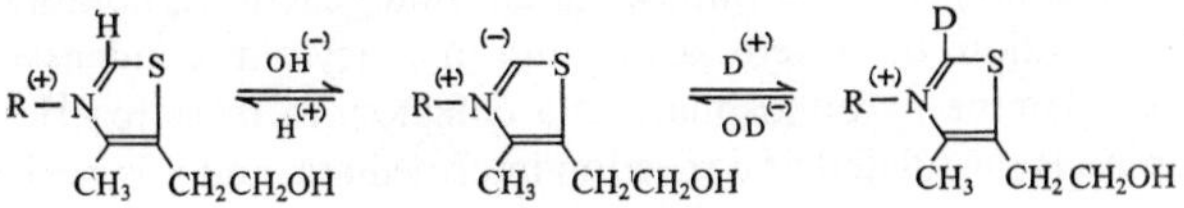

(XXI)

N-Benzyl thiazolium salts exchange the proton at C_2 more rapidly than their N-methyl analogues due to the inductive effect of the aromatic ring, which suggests one function of the pyrimidine ring in the coenzyme during biological reactions (59).

The anion or ylid (XXI) is nucleophilic and can attack an electron deficient centre such as a carbonyl group. The biochemical implications of this reaction are discussed in the following section.

Hydroxide ions can also attack the C_2 position of the thiazolium ring leading to ring cleavage (60).

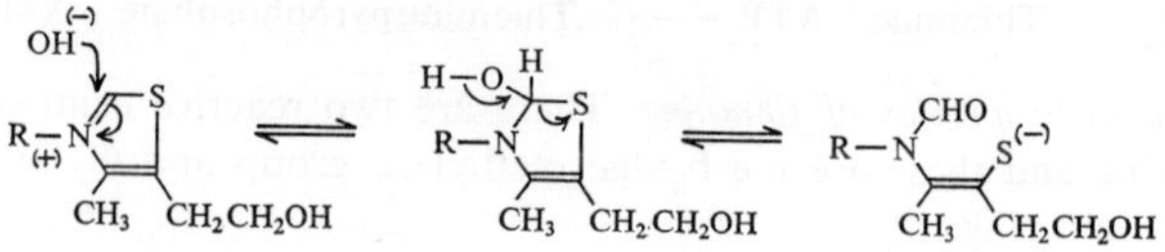

(XXII)

This explains the unusual behaviour of thiamine on treatment with alkali, three equivalents of alkali are consumed and salts of the open chain sulphide (XXII) have been isolated (61).

Alkaline solutions of thiamine are readily oxidized to the disulphide (XXIII) (61). This reaction is reversible and thiamine can be recovered from the disulphide by reduction.

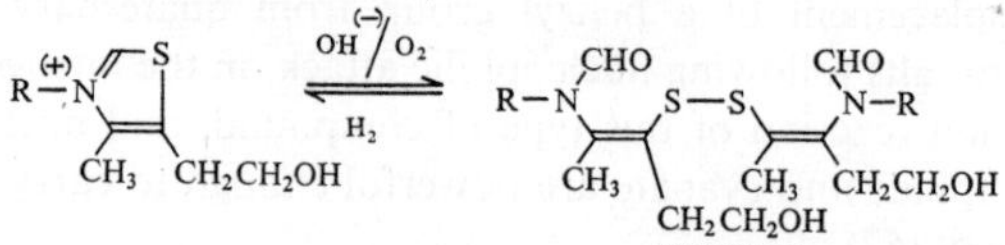

(XXIII)

There is, as yet, no definite evidence that this oxidation-reduction system plays an important part in the reactions of thiamine pyrophosphate *in vivo*.

Biochemical properties. A number of enzymic reactions, notably the decarboxylation of α-keto acids and the acyloin condensation, require thiamine pyrophosphate as a cofactor. In these reactions a carbanion is postulated as a reaction intermediate, and it is probable that the main function of thiamine pyrophosphate *in vivo* is to produce carbanions in a stabilized form.

The decarboxylation of α-keto acids, such as pyruvate, is catalysed *in vitro* by amines, and this observation led to the first suggestion as to the mechanism of action of thiamine *in vivo*. In this scheme, the 6-amino group of the pyridimine moiety formed a Schiff base with the keto acid which then lost carbon dioxide. This proposal was disproved when it was shown that thiamine did not catalyse the decarboxylation of α-keto acids *in vitro* (62).

The rapid base-catalysed exchange of the proton on the C_2 carbon atom of the thiazolium ring led Breslow to suggest that the ylid (XXI) is the active species in these enzymic reactions which require thiamine pyrophosphate as cofactor. The ylid (XXI) reacts first with pyruvate

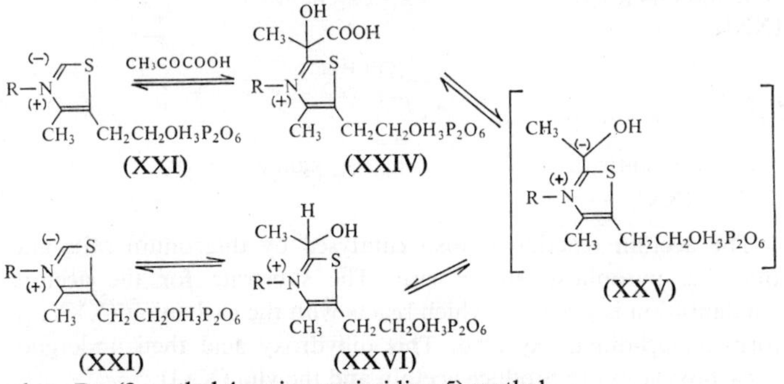

where R = (2-methyl 4-amino pyrimidine-5) methyl

to give an α-hydroxy acid (XXIV) which then loses carbon dioxide to leave the carbanion (XXV). This carbanion is stabilized by the aromaticity of the thiazolium ring, and can break down after protonation to regenerate the ylid (XXI) and liberate acetaldehyde (58).

Evidence has been obtained from deuterium exchange reactions which indicates that the ylid (XXI) is an intermediate in the decarboxylation of pyruvate *in vivo* (63).

The benzoin condensation is another example of a reaction in which a carbanion is an intermediate.

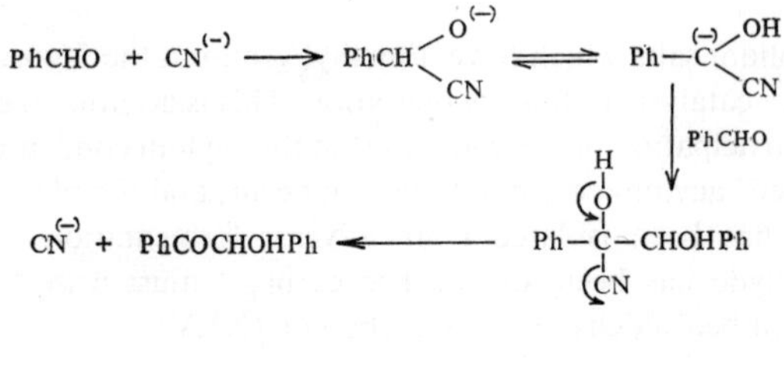

Thiazolium salts will catalyse the benzoin condensation (64), and the ylid (XXI) could play the same role as a cyanide ion in this reaction (58).

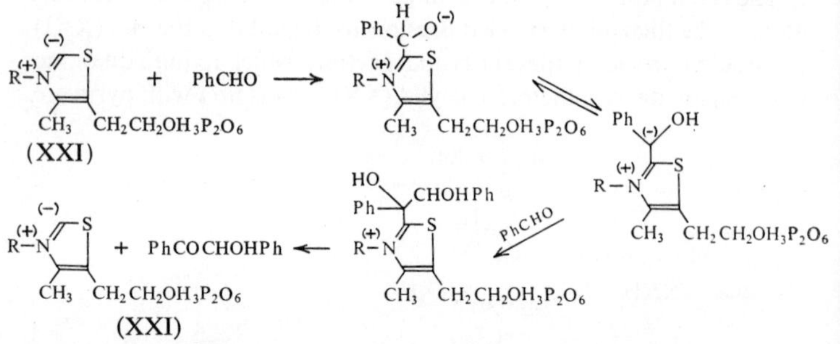

The acetoin reaction is also catalysed by thiazolium salts and thiamine pyrophosphate *in vivo*. The substrate for the acetoin condensation is pyruvate which reacts with the carbanion (XXV) to form an $\alpha\beta$-dihydroxy acid. This dihydroxy acid then undergoes decarboxylation to produce acetoin and the ylid (XXI).

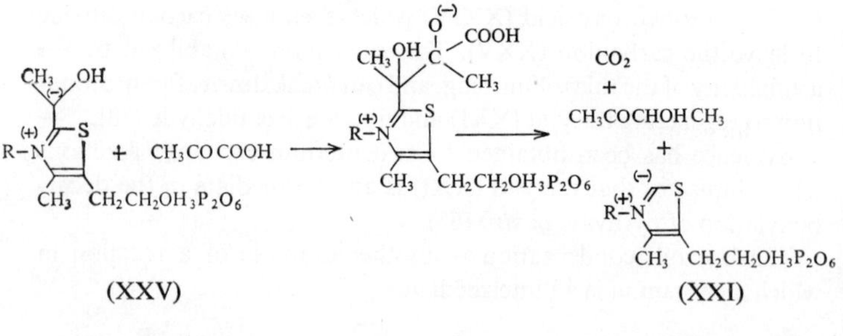

Thiazolium salts which have a methyl group in the 2 position are inactive as catalysts in this condensation. This is additional evidence for the participation of the ylid (XXI) in the acyloin condensation.

'Crossed' acyloin condensations can occur, and the phenyl acetyl carbinol has been isolated from a yeast fermentation to which benzaldehyde has been added. The carbinol must arise from the addition of benzaldehyde to the carbanion (XXV).

The role of thiamine pyrophosphate in the oxidative decarboxylation of α-keto acids can be explained in terms of the participation of the carbanion (XXV). Oxidation of this carbanion would give rise to the pyrophosphate of 2-acetyl thiamine (XXVII) which is a very powerful acetylating agent (65).

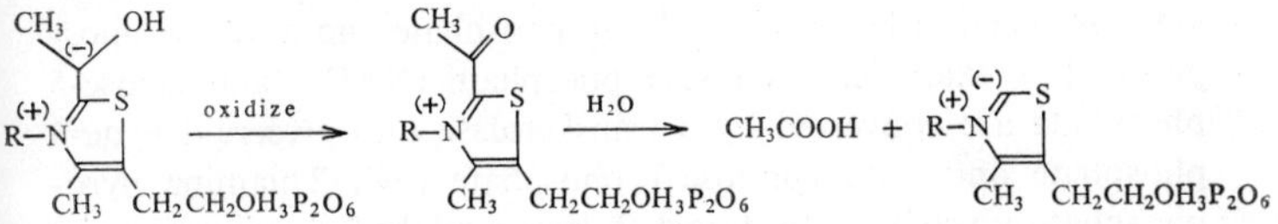

(XXV) (XXVII) (XXI)

The 2-acetyl thiamine pyrophosphate reacts rapidly with water to give the coenzyme and acetate. The isolation of 2-(β-hydroxyethyl) thiamine pyrophosphate from the reaction of pyruvate oxidase with pyruvate is strong support for the participation of the carbanion (XXV) in the oxidative decarboxylation of pyruvate (66).

The pyruvate oxidase enzyme system of *Escherichia Coli* requires thiamine pyrophosphate, lipoic acid, CoA, and NAD^+ as cofactors. The enzymic complex has been resolved into three main reactions, but thiamine pyrophosphate is required in only one of these (67). The addition product of thiamine pyrophosphate and pyruvate is oxidized by lipoic acid to 2-acetyl thiamine pyrophosphate, which acetylates the reduced lipoic acid. The acetylated, reduced lipoic acid transfers its acetyl group to CoA, and is then oxidized back to lipoic acid by NAD^+.

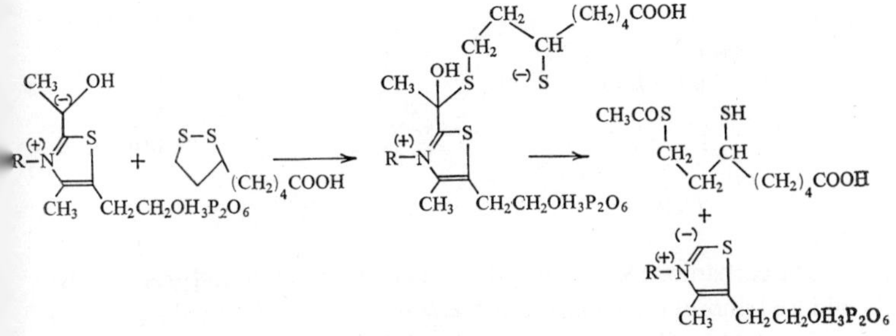

(XXV) (XXVIII) (XXI)

An alternative explanation of this reaction requires an initial interaction between the carbanion (XXV) (instead of 2-acetyl thiamine pyrophosphate) and lipoic acid to give the semithioketal (XXVIII). Breakdown of the thioketal gives rise to the ylid (XXI) and reduced acetyl lipoic acid (68).

An important stage in carbohydrate metabolism is the trans-ketolase reaction between an aldose phosphate and a ketose phosphate. For example, xylulose-5 phosphate (XXIX) and ribose-5 phosphate are converted by a transketolase into glyceraldehyde-3 phosphate and sedoheptulose-7 phosphate (69). Thiamine pyrophosphate is a cofactor for transketolases, and the following mechanism is a probable one.

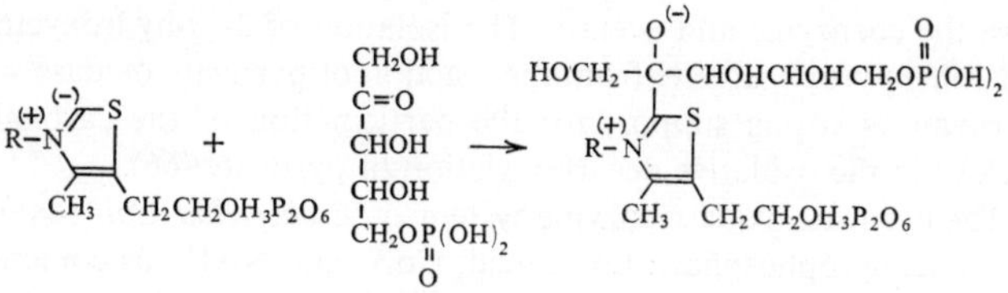

Addition of the ylid (XXI) to the carbonyl group of the ketose (xylulose) phosphate gives the product (XXX). Elimination of glyceraldehyde-3 phosphate gives rise to a carbanion (XXXI) which is stabilized by the thiazolium ring.

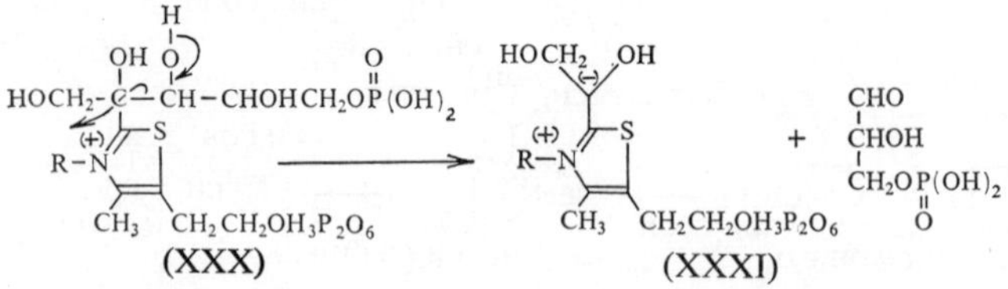

The carbanion (XXXI) can then add on to the carbonyl group of the aldose (ribose) phosphate and the addition product breaks down to sedoheptulose-7 phosphate and the ylid (XXI).

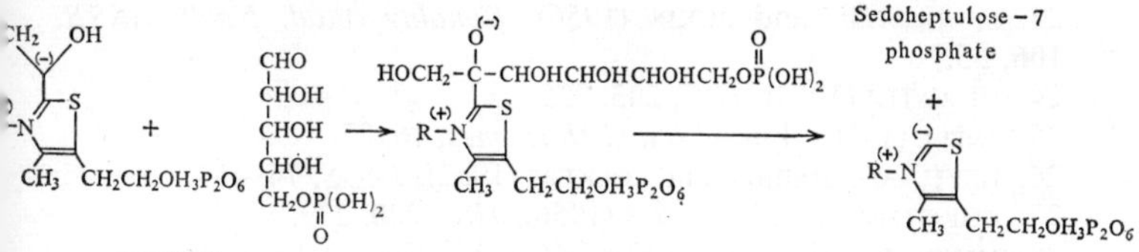

(XXXI)   (XXI)

Thus there is an overwhelming weight of evidence to support Breslow's mechanism for the mode of action of thiamine pyrophosphate in living organisms. The nature and function of the apoenzyme for thiamine pyrophosphate are, however, unknown at the present time.

REFERENCES

1. GYÖRGY (1935), *BJ*, **29**, 760.
2. KUHN and WENDT (1938), *Ber.*, **71**, 1534.
3. KUHN and WENDT (1939), *Ber.*, **72**, 305.
4. KUHN, ANDERSAG, WESTPHAL, and WENDT (1939), *Ber.*, **72**, 309.
5. KUHN, WENDT, and WESTPHAL (1939), *Ber.*, **72**, 310.
6. STILLER, KERESZTESY, and STEVENS (1939), *JACS*, **61**, 1237.
7. KUHN, WESTPHAL, WENDT, and WESTPHAL (1939), *Naturwiss.*, **27**, 469.
8. MÖLLER (1939), *Z. Physiol. Chemie*, **260**, 246.
9. ATKIN, SCHULTZ, and FREY (1939), *JACS*, **61**, 1931.
10. SNELL, GUIRARD, and WILLIAMS (1942), *JBC*, **143**, 519.
11. SNELL (1944,) *JACS*, **66**, 2082.
12. HARRIS, HEYL, and FOLKERS (1944), *JACS*, **66**, 2088.
13. SNELL (1945), *JACS*, **67**, 194.
14. SCHLENK and SNELL (1945), *JBC*, **157**, 425.
15. GUNSALUS, UMBREIT, BELLAMY, and FAUST (1945), *JBC*, **161**, 743.
16. LICHSTEIN, GUNSALUS, and UMBREIT (1945), *JBC*, **161**, 311.
17. UMBREIT and GUNSALUS (1945), *JBC*, **159**, 333.
18. BADDILEY and MATHAIS (1952), *JCS*, 2583.
19. PETERSON, SOBER, and MEISTER (1952), *JACS*, **74**, 570.
20. PETERSON, SOBER, and MEISTER (1953), *Biochem. Preps.*, **3**, 29.
21. HEYL, LUZ, HARRIS, and FOLKERS (1951), *JACS*, **73**, 3436.
22. HOLDEN and SNELL (1949), *JBC*, **178**, 799.

23. BRAUNSTEIN and BUKIN (1956), *Dokaldy Akad. Nauk. SSSR*, **106**, 95.

24. HURWITZ (1953), *JBC*, **205**, 935.

25. SNELL (1958), *Vitamins and Hormones*, **16**, 77.

26. HEYL, LUZ, HARRIS, and FOLKERS (1952), *JACS*, **74**, 414.

27. CHRISTENSEN and COLLINS (1956), *JBC*, **220**, 279.

28. METZLER and SNELL (1952), *JACS*, **74**, 979.

29. METZLER, IKAWA, and SNELL (1954), *JACS*, **76**, 648.

30. METZLER and SNELL (1952), *JBC*, **198**, 353.

31. BRAUNSTEIN (1960), *The Enzymes*, **2**, 154.

32. HILTON, BARNES, HENRY, and ENNS (1954), *JBC*, **209**, 743.

33. MEISTER (1957), *Biochemistry of the Amino Acids*, Academic Press, N.Y.

34. MANDELES, KOPPELMAN, and HANKE (1954), *JBC*, **209**, 327.

35. BERG (1953), *JBC*, **205**, 145.

36. METZLER, LONGENECKER, and SNELL (1954), *JACS*, **76**, 639.

37. SNELL (1961), *The Mechanism of Action of Water Soluble Vitamins*, Churchill, London, p. 18.

38. BRUICE and TOPPING (1963), *JACS*, **85**, 1480.

39. MEISTER, SOBER, and PETERSON (1952), *JACS*, **74**, 2385.

40. MCNUTT and SNELL (1948), *JBC*, **173**, 801.

41. JANSEN and DONATH (1926), *Verslag Akad. Wetenschapen Amsterdam*, **35**, 923.

42. WINDAUS, TSCHETSCHE, and GREWE (1934), *Z. Physiol. Chem.*, **228**, 27.

43. WILLIAMS (1935), *JACS*, **57**, 229.

44. CLARKE and GURIN (1935), *JACS*, **57**, 1876.

45. WILLIAMS (1936), *JACS*, **58**, 1063.

46. CLINE, WILLIAMS, AND FINKELSTEIN (1937), *JACS*, **59**, 1052.

47. ANDERSAG and WESTPHAL (1937), *Ber.*, **70**, 2035.

48. TODD and BERGEL (1937), *JCS*, 364.

49. LOHMANN and SCHUSTER (1937), *Biochem. Z.*, **294**, 188.

50. BANGA, OCHOA, and PETERS (1939), *BJ*, **33**, 1109.

51. VISCONTINI, BONETTI, and KARRER (1949), *Helv. Chim. Acta*, **32**, 1478.

52. ROSSI-FANELLI, SILIPRANDI, SILIPRANDI, and CICCARONE (1955), *Arch. Biochem. Biophys.*, **58**, 237.

53. HARRIS and YAVIT (1957), *Fed. Proc.*, **16**, 192.

54. LEDER (1959), *Fed. Proc.*, **18**, 270.

55. CAMIENER and BROWN (1959), *JACS*, **81**, 3800.

56. BROWN (1962), *Ann. N.Y. Acad. Sci.*, **98**, 485.

57. SYNDER and SPECK (1939), *JACS*, **61**, 2895.

58. BRESLOW (1958), *JACS*, **80**, 3719.

59. BRESLOW and MCNELIS (1959), *JACS*, **81**, 3080.

60. WATANABE and ASAHI (1955), *J. Pharm. Soc. Japan*, **75**, 1050.

61. ZIMA and WILLIAMS (1940), *Ber.*, **73**, 941.

62. STERN and MELNICK (1939), *JBC*, **131**, 597.

63. FRY (1963), *Diss. Abs.*, **23**, 2309.

64. UGAI, TANAKA, and DOKAWA (1943), *J. Pharm. Soc. Japan*, **63**, 269.

65. DAIGO and REED (1962), *JACS*, **84**, 659.

66. HOLZER, DA FANESCA-WOLLHEIM, KOHLHAW, and WOENCKHAUS, (1962), *Ann. N.Y. Acad. Sci.*, **98**, 453.

67. METZLER (1960), *The Enzymes*, **2**, 315.

68. WHITE and INGRAHAM (1962), *JACS*, **84**, 3109.

69. HORECKER, SMYRNIOTIS, and KLENOW (1953), *JBC*, **205**, 661.

CHAPTER FIVE

Oligo- and Polynucleotides

5.1 Introduction

The important role of nucleic acids in the transference of genetic information and in the biosynthesis of proteins has stimulated the study of the detailed chemistry of oligo- and polynucleotides in an attempt to gain some insight into the mode of action of nucleic acids in living organisms.

The elucidation of the sequence of mononucleotides in a given nucleic acid is an extremely difficult problem to solve by purely chemical methods. If the molecular weight of the nucleic acid is assumed to be 100,000, the number of mononucleotides present in the polymer must be between 250 and 300. The number of permutations of nucleotide sequence, using only the four main purine and pyrimidine nucleotides, is of the order of 50×10^8. At the present time no chemical method of analysis exists for the determination of such a sequence of closely similar compounds, and a more promising approach is by hydrolysis with specific enzymes.

The ribonucleic acids which act as templates in the biosynthesis of protein, 'transfer-RNAs', are of comparatively low molecular weight (30,000) and contain about 80 nucleotides in each polymer chain. It is possible, therefore, that partial degradation of these transfer-RNAs by enzymic means to oligonucleotides of known composition will yield valuable information concerning the structure of the macromolecule.

The problem of nucleotide sequence could, conceivably, be solved by X-ray crystallography and much valuable information about polynucleotides has already been obtained by this technique, for example, the helical coil structure of DNA. Here again, technical difficulties are severe and no complete structure of a polynucleotide has been determined by X-ray crystallography at the present time.

5.2 The nature of the internucleotide bond

The structure of polynucleotides and, in particular, the nature of the internucleotide bond, was a matter of considerable speculation until the problem was resolved by Brown and Todd in 1952 (1).

Degradation studies by Levene and Harris had led to the belief that only four nucleotides could be isolated from polynucleotides by either chemical or enzymic hydrolysis, and that these nucleotides were all nucleoside-3' phosphates (2). With the advent of ion-exchange chromatography, it became apparent that isomeric pairs of nucleotides were present in the alkaline hydrolysates of RNA (3); and these isomeric pairs were shown to be ribonucleoside-2' and -3' phosphates (4). Hydrolysis of RNA by ribonuclease followed by further hydrolysis with intestinal phosphodiesterase gave the ribonucleoside-5' phosphates (5). RNA when treated with rattlesnake (*Crotalus adamanteus*) venom phosphodiesterase also gave ribo-nucleoside-5' phosphates, together with free ribonucleosides and ribonucleoside-2'(3)',5' diphosphates (6). Thus the 5' position was definitely involved in the internucleotide linkage in RNA, and the 5' position of one ribonucleoside was possibly joined by a phosphate group to either the 2',3', or 5' hydroxyls of the adjacent ribonucleoside.

Glycerol-1 and -2 phosphates undergo a rapid intramolecular isomerization proceeding through the cyclic phosphate (7); and although glycerol-1 phosphoric acid is stable to alkali, the mono-methyl ester (a phosphodiester) is hydrolysed rapidly to a mixture of glycerol-1 and -2 phosphoric acids and methanol (8). RNA, in contrast to DNA, undergoes rapid alkaline hydrolysis to a mixture of ribonucleoside-2' and -3' phosphates. Similarly, both ribonucleo-side-2' benzyl phosphates and ribonucleoside-3' benzyl phosphates undergo rapid alkaline hydrolysis to benzyl alcohol and a mixture of the ribonucleoside-2' and -3' phosphates (1). The intermediate ribonucleoside-2',3' cyclic phosphates have been synthesized, and decompose in alkali to a mixture of ribonucleoside-2' and -3' phosphates (9).

Brown and Todd (1) proposed that the sugar moieties of successive ribonucleosides were joined by a phosphodiester group which linked the 3' and 5' hydroxyl groups; alkaline degradation would cleave the

8

internucleotide bond to give ribonucleoside-2′, 3′ cyclic phosphates. These cyclic phosphates could then be attacked by the alkali to give a mixture of ribonucleoside-2′ and -3′ phosphates.

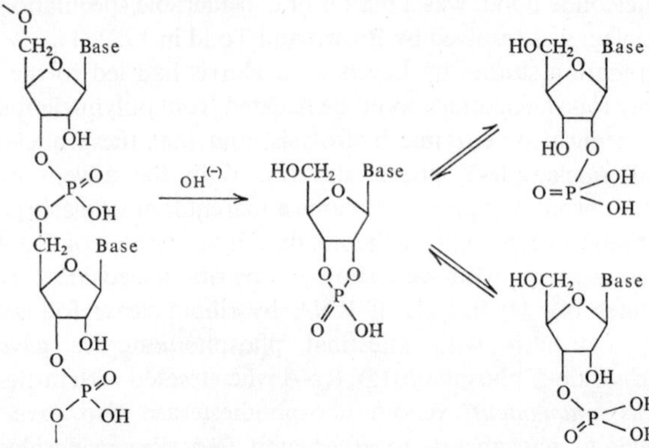

Enzymic cleavage of RNA can give rise to either ribonucleoside-3′ or -5′ phosphates, and will be discussed in more detail in Section 4 of this chapter.

The presence of a free hydroxyl group on the sugar moiety adjacent to the phosphodiester linkage is required for rapid alkaline hydrolysis of RNA, as both DNA and synthetic dinucleotides, such as adenylyl (5′→5′) uridine, are stable to alkali (10). This excludes the possibility of 5′→5′ linkages in RNA.

The isolation of ribonucleoside-5′ phosphates from enzymic hydrolysates of RNA excludes the possibility of 2′→2′ and 3′→3′ links except as very minor components.

Spleen phosphodiesterase is an enzyme which specifically attacks ribonucleoside-3′ phosphate, and not ribonucleoside-2′ phosphate, diesters (11). RNA is hydrolysed by this enzyme and hence the 2′→5′ linkage is excluded for RNA.

The structure of DNA was postulated, by analogy with RNA, to be a polynucleotide with the successive deoxyribonucleosides joined by a 3′→5′ phosphodiester link. This proposal has been proved to be correct by enzymic degradation with both spleen and rattlesnake venom phosphodiesterases, and by X-ray crystallography (12).

5.3 Chemical degradation of polynucleotides

The most straightforward method of determination of the sequence of monomeric units in a polymer is by stepwise degradation. This can be represented schematically as follows, where N_x are monomeric subunits (nucleotides) of the polymer (polynucleotide).

$$N_1-N_2-N_3-N_4-N_5-N_6 \longrightarrow N_1-N_2-N_3-N_4-N_5 + N_6$$

$$N_1-N_2-N_3-N_4-N_5 \longrightarrow N_1-N_2-N_3-N_4 + N_5 \quad etc.$$

An alternative method is to degrade the polymer into subunits (oligonucleotides) and identify each of the subunits by further degradation.

$$N_1-N_2-N_3-N_4-N_5-N_6 \to \begin{cases} N_1-N_2-N_3 + N_4-N_5-N_6 \\ N_1-N_2 + N_3-N_4 + N_5-N_6 \\ N_1-N_2 + N_2-N_3 + N_3-N_4 + N_4-N_5 + N_5-N_6 \end{cases}$$

Examination of the sequence of monomeric units in each of the smaller subunits can then lead to the structure of the polymer.

Both these methods have been used in the structural determination of peptides and proteins (13) but have not yet been applied successfully to polynucleotides.

One drawback in the stepwise degradation of polynucleotides is that none of the chemical degradation reactions, which have been developed at the present time, are quantitative. Thus after the first three or four mononucleotides have been identified, there is such contamination from partially degraded polynucleotides that precise identification of further mononucleotides is difficult.

The first successful method to be developed for the identification of the terminal nucleotide of a polyribonucleotide consists of the fission of the *cis*-glycol of the D-ribose moiety with neutral metaperiodate, followed by the elimination of the purine or pyrimidine base at pH 10.

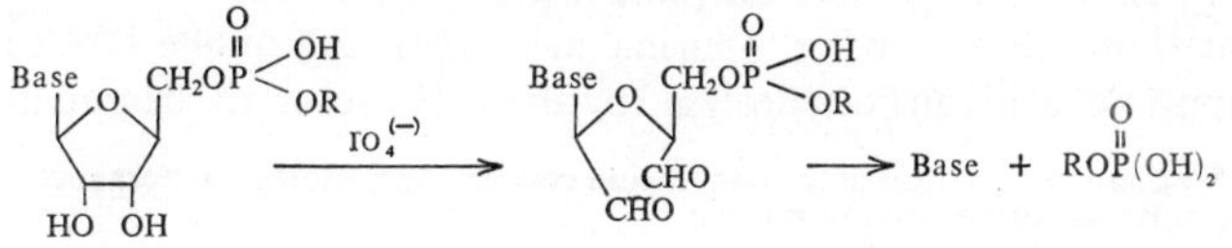

If one of the hydroxyls of the *cis*-glycol is blocked by a phospho-monoester group, this can be removed enzymically before the reaction with metaperiodate (14, 15).

In a modification of this method, the dialdehyde which can be obtained by the action of metaperiodate on a polyribonucleotide is treated with an excess of a primary amine in aqueous solution. The terminal base is then released (16). This modification was applied to the degradation of transfer-RNA, and revealed that the terminal nucleotides in the RNA chain are CpCpA* and that either the 2′ or the 3′ hydroxyl group of the terminal adenosine moiety was esterified by an amino acid (16).

This method of stepwise degradation is, of course, not applicable to polydeoxyribonucleotides as the *cis*-glycol function is absent. However, a method for the sequential degradation of polynucleotides which depends on the oxidation of the terminal 5′ hydroxyl group of the polymer is, in theory, applicable to both the ribo- and deoxyribo-series (17, 18). Elimination of the terminal base from the 5′ carboxylic acid does not take place smoothly unless the acid is first converted into an amide (18). The 5′ amide, after heating in alkali, does break down to release the terminal base, but the reactions conditions are severe and this method has not found wide application.

Another approach to the partial degradation of polynucleotides is to remove, selectively, either the purine or the pyrimidine base leaving a polymer consisting of a sugar-phosphate backbone with only one type of base attached to the backbone.

In dilute aqueous acid the purines are eliminated from DNA (but not from RNA) leaving 'apurinic acid' (19), and unlike DNA the 'apurinic' acid can be hydrolysed by alkali. However, the degradation

* For an explanation of the convention concerning a shorthand nomenclature for polynucleotides see the Preface.

is complex and unspecific hydrolysis can take place at the same time as the elimination of the purines.

A more successful method of degrading DNA by means of 'apurinic' acid has been developed by Burton (20) from the Dische colour reaction for DNA (21, 22). The Dische colorimetric method for the assay of DNA depends on the estimation of the blue colour (23) produced by the reaction between diphenylamine and DNA in acid solution. The purine bases are eliminated in acid solution, and it appears that the diphenylamine reacts with the sugar residues which were originally attached to the purines, as no colour is produced when thymidylic acid is used in place of DNA in this reaction (22). Burton observed that elimination of inorganic orthophosphate takes place during the reaction, and proposed that this orthophosphate arose from the fission of the phosphate bridge between two adjacent purine nucleotides in the polynucleotide chain. Approximately 25 % of the total phosphorus in DNA is liberated in this way, which provides support for the theory that there is a random distribution of purine and pyrimidine base in DNA.

The 'Burton' degradation has been applied to the single-stranded DNA of the bacterial virus ϕ XI74 by Hall and Sinsheimer (24). The DNA was degraded with diphenylamine in formic acid and, after the 'apurinic' acid had been hydrolysed enzymically, the oligonucleotide mixture was separated into its components by chromatography. From the composition of these components, and in particular the high number of polypyrimidine oligonucleotides, Hall and Sinsheimer conclude that there is not a random distribution of nucleotides in this DNA.

Pyrimidines react with hydrazine to yield a pyrazolone and urea (25, 26), and this reaction has been applied both to nucleosides (14) and nucleic acids (27, 28). The sugar moieties of nucleosides form hydrazones with hydrazine and a polymeric 'apyrimidinic' acid is formed from nucleic acids. The 'apyrimidinic' acid can be hydrolysed by alkali after the removal of the hydrazine residue by benzaldehyde. This method has been used as a specific partial hydrolysis procedure for the degradation of transfer-RNA and DNA.

Hydrolysis of polynucleotides by acid or alkali is non-specific and can be accompanied by extensive degradation of the polymer to mononucleotides, although oligonucleotides have been isolated from the acid hydrolysates of 'apurinic' DNA (29).

5.4 Enzymic degradation of polynucleotides

There are three main classes of phosphodiesterases which can attack internucleotide bonds, these are ribonucleases, which are specific for polyribonucleotides, deoxyribonucleases which are specific for polydeoxyribonucleotides, and unspecific phosphodiesterases which hydrolyse both polyribo- and polydeoxyribonucleotides.

(a) *Ribonucleases*. Hydrolysis of RNA by ribonuclease yields ribo-nucleoside-2′,3′ cyclic phosphates and oligonucleotides which possess terminal pyrimidine nucleoside-3′ or pyrimidine nucleoside-2′,3′ cyclic phosphates (30, 31). The pyrimidine nucleoside-3′ phosphates arise from the slow hydrolysis of the cyclic-2′,3′ phosphates (32).

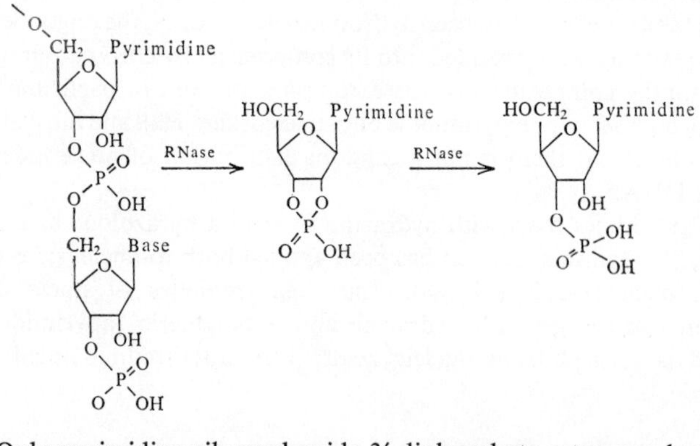

Only pyrimidine ribonucleoside-3′ diphosphate esters are hydrolysed by RNase (33); this specificity for *pyrimidine* ribonucleoside-3′ phosphates and the formation of small oligonucleotides during hydrolysis reaction (31) make hydrolysis by ribonuclease a promising approach for the structural determination of polyribonucleotides.

A ribonuclease has been reported which will hydrolyse RNA to nucleoside-5′ phosphates (34), but it is not certain whether this enzyme is a specific ribonuclease or whether it is able to degrade polydeoxyribonucleotides. If this is the case, it is then a member of the third class of enzymes described in this section, the unspecific phosphodiesterases.

(b) *Deoxyribonucleases*. There are two types of deoxyribonucleases, those for which the final hydrolysis products (mononucleotides) are 5′-phosphomonoesters and those for which the final hydrolysis products are 3′-phosphomonoesters.

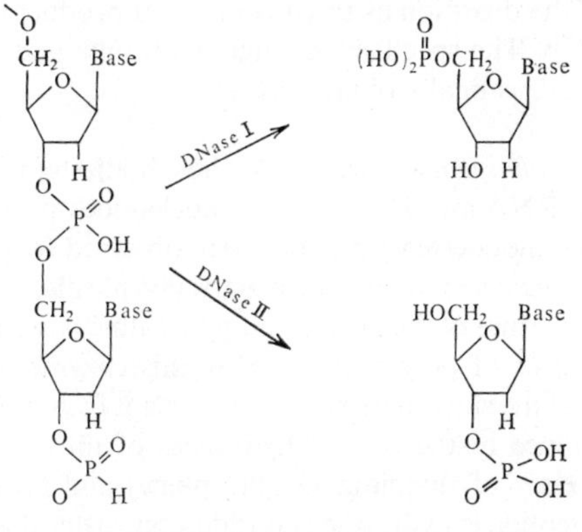

Deoxyribonuclease type I (DNase I) has been isolated in a crystalline form from bovine pancreas (35) and will hydrolyse DNA to small oligonucleotides bearing a 5′-phosphomonoester group (36). This pancreatic deoxyribonuclease will attack all tetra-nucleotides and higher homologues which possess a 5′-phosphomonoester end group (37); di- and tri-nucleotides with this end group are unaffected. Cleavage occurs at internal bonds; for example, tetra-nucleotides give mainly dinucleotides, and penta-nucleotides give a mixture of di- and tri-nucleotides. In a series of homologues, the rate of hydrolysis increases with chain length and purine polydeoxyribonucleotides are hydrolysed at a faster rate than their pyrimidine counterparts. The enzyme will also hydrolyse TpTpTpTp, a polynucleotide bearing a 3′-phosphomonoester group, which indicates that the nature of the group attached to the 3′-phosphomonoester of the substrate is not critical for enzymic activity. Thus TpTpTpTp is equivalent to TpTpTpTpT.

DNase I has a pH optimum of 7, and a second type of DNase, DNase II, with a pH optimum of 4·5 to 5·5 has been isolated from spleen and other sources (38, 39, 40). The DNase II hydrolyses DNA to 3′-phosphomonoesters in a two-stage process. About one-tenth of the internucleotide bonds are hydrolysed rapidly and the resulting oligonucleotides are then hydrolysed at a much slower rate. The d-GpGp bonds appear to be cleaved preferentially at the beginning of the digestion as the predominant product is of the type d-Gp(Xp)n-Gp. The specificity changes with time and a mixture of oligonucleotides is finally obtained (41).

(c) *Unspecific phosphodiesterases.* A phosphodiesterase which will degrade both RNA and DNA to oligonucleotides possessing a terminal phosphomonoester group has been obtained from rattlesnake (*Crotalus adamanteus*) venom in a partially purified form (6, 42). Although the nature of the purine and pyrimidine bases is not critical in the hydrolysis of polynucleotides by this enzyme, the chemical constitution of the sugar moiety is an important factor. This is shown by the difference in the rate of hydrolysis of nitrophenyl-pT (the nitrophenyl ester of thymidine-5′ phosphate) and nitrophenyl-pU. The ribonucleotide is hydrolysed considerably faster than the deoxyribonucleotide, indicating that the presence of a 2′ hydroxyl group accelerates the hydrolysis by the enzyme. Acetylation of the 3′ hydroxyl of nitrophenyl-pT slows down the rate of hydrolysis, and oligonucleotides bearing 3′-phosphomonoester end groups are resistant to the enzyme (32, 43).

It appears that the rattlesnake venom phosphodiesterase possesses a prosthetic group which binds to a free 3′ hydroxyl group before hydrolysis can take place. Thus, the 2′ hydroxyl in nitrophenyl-pU is, by its proximity to the 3′ hydroxyl, a serious competitor for this prosthetic group and hence the rate of hydrolysis is lowered. If the 5' hydroxyl group of either a ribo- or deoxyribonucleotide is vacant this can also act as a competitor for the prosthetic group, though it is not in such a sterically favourable position as the 3' position. Di-nucleotide phosphates such as TpT are hydrolysed more slowly than the corresponding di-nucleotide which possess a 5' phosphate end group (44).

Spleen phosphodiesterase degrades both polyribo-and poly-deoxyribonucleotides provided the terminal 5' hydroxyl group is unesterified (45). The requirement of a free 5' hydroxyl is critical, and polynucleotides bearing 5' phosphomonoester groups are not de-graded by this enzyme (46). Spleen phosphodiesterase hydrolyses the polynucleotide in a stepwise fashion from the end bearing the free 5' hydroxyl group, and hence it is probable that the prosthetic group of this enzyme binds to the 3' phosphomonoester at the other end of the polynucleotide (45).

From the evidence outlined in this section, it is apparent that sequence determination of polynucleotides by specific enzymic hydrolysis is a feasible proposition. The sequential determination, however, requires the separation of very similar oligonucleotides and this is an extremely difficult and tedious process using the techniques which are available at the present time.

5.5 Chemical synthesis of polynucleotides

In a naturally occurring polynucleotide, the 3' and 5' hydroxyl groups of successive nucleosides are joined by phosphate residues. An important problem in the chemical synthesis of polynucleotides is the protection of other groups (notably the 2' hydroxyl in ribo-nucleosides) in the monomer molecule in order to achieve the specific 3' → 5' phosphodiester linkage.

The problem is simplified in the case of polydeoxyribonucleotides owing to the absence of the 2' hydroxyl group; in addition, the differences in reactivity between the primary (5') alcohol and the secondary (3') alcohol can be used in the preparation of suitably protected deoxyribonucleosides. It is for these two reasons that much of the work on the synthesis of polynucleotides has been devoted to the synthesis of polydeoxyribonucleotides.

The most obvious approach to the synthesis of a phosphodiester is to treat suitably protected nucleosides with a bifunctional phosphorylating agent followed by the removal of the protecting groups. This method has been employed for the synthesis of uridylyl ($5' \rightarrow 5'$) uridine, when 2',3'-benzylidene uridine was treated with phenyl phosphorodichloridate (47). A variation of this process is the treatment of an alkyl halide with the silver salt of a protected nucleoside phosphate, and adenylyl ($5' \rightarrow 5'$) uridine has been prepared by this method (10).

Nucleoside-5' phosphorochloridates have also been used in the preparation of dinucleoside phosphates (48). Benzyl 2',3-isopropylidene adenosine-5' phosphite (49) (I) can be readily chlorinated to the phosphorochloride (II) which is a phosphorylating agent. This is a second route to adenylyl ($5' \rightarrow 5'$) uridine and thymidylyl ($3' \rightarrow 5'$) thymidine has also been prepared in this manner (50). Although this

(I)   (II)

method has been extended to the preparation of thymidylyl ($3' \rightarrow 5'$) thymidine-3' phosphate (TpTp), it is unsatisfactory for the preparation of larger oligonucleotides and has now been superseded by methods using carbodiimides.

Khorana and his co-workers have used carbodiimides and acid anhydrides for the formation of the $3' \rightarrow 5'$ internucleotide link with success (51). Thymidylyl ($3' \rightarrow 5'$) thymidine (TpT) has been synthesized by this group by the action of dicyclohexyl carbodiimide or *p*-toluene sulphonyl chloride on a mixture of 3'-acetyl thymidine-5' phosphate (III) and 5'-trityl thymidine (IV), followed by the removal of the protecting groups first with alkali (acetyl removal) and then acid (trityl removal) (52).

If dibenzyl thymidine-5' phosphate is used instead of 5'-trityl thymidine in this reaction, pTpT can be obtained after removal of the acetyl group by alkaline hydrolysis and the benzyl groups by hydrogenolysis.

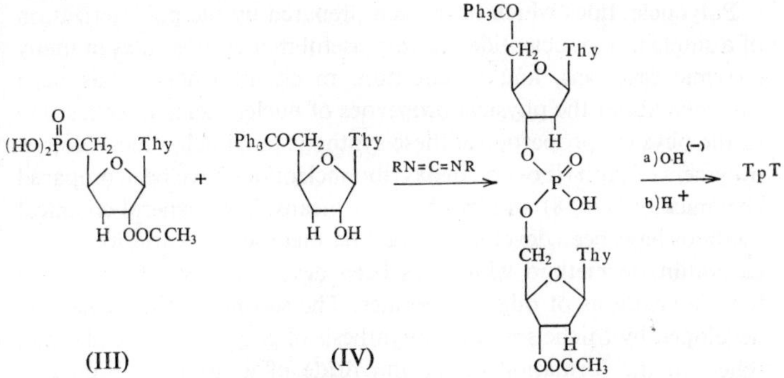

(III)   (IV)

If the fully protected dithymidine phosphate (V) is treated with alkali to remove the acetyl group, the 3′hydroxyl group which is freed can then be phosphorylated. A convenient phosphorylating system is β-cyanoethyl phosphate and dicyclohexyl carbodiimide: the β-cyanoethyl moiety is readily split off from the oligonucleotide in alkaline solution (53).

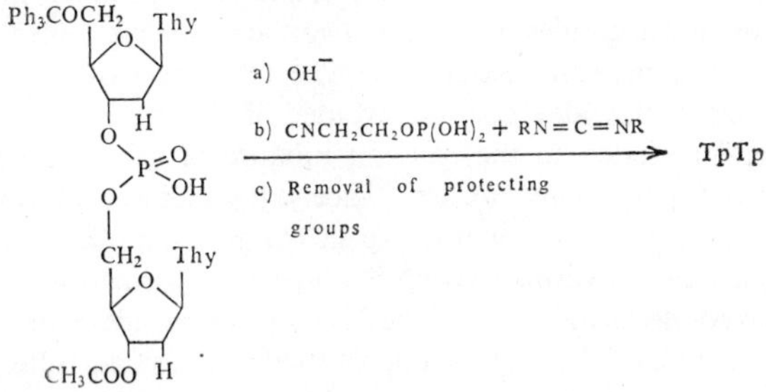

(V)

Tri-nucleotides can be prepared by substituting a nucleoside phosphate for β-cyanoethyl phosphate in the final phosphorylating step in the reaction outlined above (54).

In this manner, Khorana has been able to synthesize a variety of both oligoribonucleotides (55), and oligodeoxyribonucleotides (56) with a known sequence of bases.

Polynucleotides which have been prepared by the polymerization of a single mononucleotide are very useful model substrates in many enzymic reactions, and in addition, much information has been obtained about the physical properties of nucleic acids from a study of the physical properties of these synthetic polynucleotides. Homopolymers of both ribo- and deoxyribonucleotides have been prepared enzymically (57, 58) and by chemical means. Two general chemical methods have been developed. The first method is a variation of the carbodiimide method which has been developed by Khorana (51) for the synthesis of oligonucleotides. The second method has been developed by Michelson for the synthesis of polyribonucleotides and relies on the formation of an anhydride of a ribonucleoside-2',3' cyclic phosphate (59).

The carbodiimide route is particularly applicable to the preparation of polydeoxyribonucleotides, and a complex mixture of polymeric products has been obtained from the reaction between dicyclohexyl carbodiimide and either thymidine-3' or thymidine-5' phosphate (43, 60). Two types of polynucleotide are obtained by this method: linear oligonucleotides in which the mononucleotide residues are joined by 3'-5' phosphodiester linkages, and cyclic products in which the terminal nucleotides of a small oligonucleotide are joined to one another by a phosphodiester link. The formation of these small cyclic oligonucleotides can be avoided if 3'-acetyl thymidine-5' phosphate is added to the reaction mixture of carbodiimide and thymidine-5' phosphate (60). The 3'-acetyl thymidine-5' phosphate is incorporated as the terminal group in the growing oligonucleotide and, as a free 3' hydroxyl group is absent, the formation of cyclic oligonucleotides is inhibited. If the 3'-acetyl nucleoside-5' phosphate contains a different base to the unprotected nucleoside-5' phosphate, oligonucleotides with specific terminal nucleotides can be obtained. Symmetrical P^1, P^2-dithymidine pyrophosphates are also formed during the reaction and complicate the separation of the oligo- and polynucleotides by ion-exchange chromatography. These pyrophosphates can be destroyed by treating the reaction mixture with an excess of acetic anhydride, before the ion-exchange separation (61).

Mixed anhydrides, such as p-toluene sulphonyl chloride or diphenyl phosphorchloridate, are also capable of polymerizing thymidine-5′ phosphate, but appear to produce oligonucleotides with a lower degree of polymerization than those obtained using dicyclohexyl carbodiimide.

By the polymerization of dinucleotide phosphates with dicyclohexyl carbodiimide, Khorana has prepared copolymers of known base sequence, for example, d-pTpApTpA (62).

The carbodiimide method is unsatisfactory for the preparation of homopolymers of ribonucleotides as polymer formation is inhibited by the ready formation of nucleoside-2′3′ phosphates which do not react with carbodiimides as they are phosphodiesters. This problem could, in theory, be solved by the protection of the 2′ hydroxyl groups with a suitable blocking group. However, an alternative route to polyribonucleotides has been developed by Michelson which avoids this difficulty; this approach does not, however, avoid the other problem of polyribonucleotide synthesis, the simultaneous formation of 2′-5′ and 3′-5′ phosphodiester links.

Treatment of glycerol-1 or -2 phosphate with an anhydride such as diphenyl phosphorochloridate or tetraphenyl pyrophosphate yields glycerol-1,2 cyclic phosphate (63) and the addition of more anhydride with an excess of a base gives polyglycerol polyphosphate (64). By an extension of this method, Michelson has prepared polyribonucleotides, of an average chain length of twelve monomer units, from ribonucleoside-2′(3′) phosphates.

The ribonucleoside-2′,3′ cyclic phosphate (VI) is converted, by the action of the anhydride, into a fully esterified pyrophosphate (VII) which then undergoes nucleophilic attack by the 5′ hydroxyl of another molecule of the cyclic phosphate (VI) leading to a polymeric

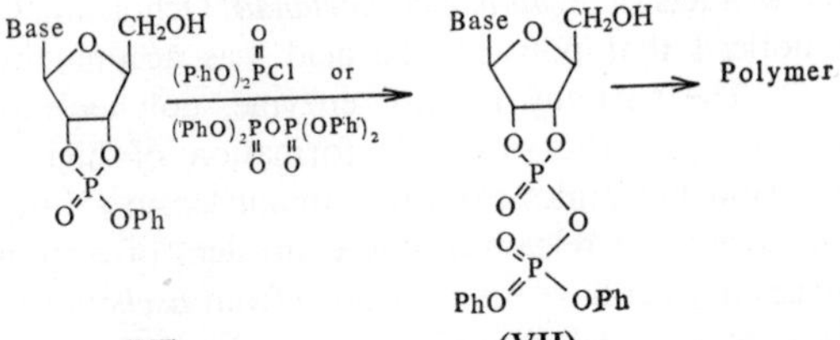

(VI)   (VII)

cyclic phosphate. Cleavage of the cyclic phosphate rings of this polymer gives rise to polymers containing either the 2'-5' or the 3'-5' phosphodiester link.

A disadvantage of this method is that interaction can occur between the anhydride initiating polymerization and another reactive group in the monomer, such as a hydroxyl or an amino group. This interaction is especially inconvenient if anhydrides other than diphenyl phosphorichloridate or tetraphenyl pyrophosphate are employed (65). Polymerization of mixtures of nucleoside-2' (3') phosphates or small oligonucleotides bearing a terminal 2'(3') phosphate gives rise to copolymers (66).

5.6 Biosynthesis of polynucleotides

Both RNA and DNA are synthesized enzymically in a manner analogous to the biosynthesis of coenzymes such as NAD^+ or FAD. The polymerization reaction consists of the displacement of a phosphoryl residue from a nucleoside-5' polyphosphate by the nucleophilic attack of a 3' hydroxyl of a second nucleoside-5' polyphosphate. There are two possible pathways by which polymerization can take place, either (i) by the attack of a 3' hydroxyl of a monomer on the polymer which terminates in a polyphosphate group, or (ii) by the attack by the 3' hydroxyl of the polymer on the monomer polyphosphate (67).

Three classes of enzyme are known which will catalyse the formation of polynucleotides; these are polynucleotide phosphorylases, DNA polymerases, and RNA polymerases.

(a) *Polynucleotide phosphorylase*. During experiments on the exchange of ^{32}P labelled orthophosphate with the terminal phosphate of ADP in dialyzed extracts of *Azotobacter vinelandii*, Ochoa and Grunberg-Manago noticed that polyadenylic acid was accumulated in the system (68). The partially purified enzyme, polynucleotide phosphorylase, catalyses the reversible formation of high molecular weight polyribonucleotides from the ribonucleoside-5' diphosphate with the concomitant release of one equivalent of orthophosphate (57). Similar enzymes have been obtained from *Escherichia Coli* (69), and *Micrococcus lysodeikticus* (70).

$$\text{n. App} \rightleftharpoons (\text{Ap})_n + \text{n.P}_i$$

Mixtures of ribonucleoside-5′ diphosphates are polymerized by polynucleotide phosphorylases to copolymers (71, 72).

Polynucleotide phosphorylase will only polymerize ribonucleoside-5′ diphosphates and not deoxyribonucleoside-5′ diphosphates or ribonucleoside-5′ triphosphates. Thymine, hypoxanthine, and pseudouracil ribonucleoside-5′ diphosphates are all polymerized by polynucleotide phosphorylase indicating that the nature of the base of the ribonucleoside-5′ diphosphate is not critical for enzymic activity (73, 74).

The high molecular weight polyribonucleotides, which are synthesized by this enzyme system, contain 3′-5′ phosphodiester linkages between successive nucleosides. This can be demonstrated by both chemical and enzymic degradation (75). X-Ray diffraction patterns of mixed purine-pyrimidine copolymers, which have been prepared by the action of polynucleotide phosphorylase, are very similar to those obtained from RNA (76). Thus, the synthetic polynucleotides have the same intra-molecular structure as their naturally occurring counterparts.

The enzyme requires a polynucleotide primer before it can synthesize additional amounts of polynucleotide; if this primer is omitted there is an induction period before polymerization takes place (77). If a small oligoribonucleotide (such as pApApA) is used as primer, no specificity is observed concerning the substrate ribonucleoside-5′ diphosphate, and poly U and poly A are produced with equal ease (78). Large polyribonucleotides, however, are more specific in their action as primers; and although poly A will initiate the polymerization of ADP, it will inhibit the polymerization of poly U completely (77). The primers must have a free 3′ hydroxyl group before polymerization of the substrate ribonucleoside-5′ diphosphates can take place (79).

The reverse reaction, the phosphorolysis of RNA, also requires the presence of a free 3′ hydroxyl in the substrate (RNA) before degradation can take place, and polyribonucleotides which terminate in a 3′ phosphomonoester group are not degraded by polynucleotide phosphorylase (80). The phosphorolysis reaction takes place by stepwise cleavage and the final products are either dinucleotides or dinucleotide phosphates (81), as the enzyme is incapable of breaking down these dimers further. This observation is consistent with the requirement of the enzyme for a polynucleotide primer before polymerization of ribonucleoside-5′ diphosphates can occur, as the enzyme is also incapable of the synthesis of polymers from monomeric subunits.

(b) *DNA polymerase*. An enzyme has been purified from *Escherichia Coli*, and is present in a variety of sources, which will incorporate the 5′ triphosphates of the four main deoxynucleotides into DNA in the presence of a primer (58).

$$\begin{bmatrix} \text{d-Appp} \\ \text{d-Gppp} \\ \text{Tppp} \\ \text{d-Cppp} \end{bmatrix} \rightleftharpoons \text{DNA} + \text{n.PP}_i$$

Inorganic pyrophosphate is released during the incorporation reaction and the reaction is reversed in the presence of a large excess of inorganic pyrophosphate.

Omission of any one of the four deoxyribonucleoside triphosphates from the enzyme system reduces the reaction rate sharply and omission of the deoxyribonucleotide primer inhibits DNA synthesis completely (82).

Calf thymus DNA polymerase will not use 'native' DNA as a primer for DNA synthesis. DNA primers suitable for the polymerization reaction can be prepared by any treatment of the double-helical 'native' DNA which produces the single-stranded non-helical form (83).

Direct inclusion of the primer into DNA has not yet been observed, and the function of the primer is a complex one as it also acts as a template for further synthesis of DNA.

Oligodeoxyribonucleotides can act as primers for the polymerization of single deoxyribonucleoside-5′ triphosphates catalysed by calf thymus DNA polymerase, provided that they are trimers or in a higher state polymerization (84).

(c) *RNA polymerase*. Two types of RNA polymerase have been observed, those which require DNA as primer and those which require RNA as primer (85).

Like DNA polymerase, the enzymes have a specific requirement for all four ribonucleoside-5′ triphosphates as substrates. The base ratios in the newly synthesized RNA indicate that both the DNA and the RNA primers are templates for the synthetic reactions in addition to their function as primers. In contrast to DNA polymerase, RNA polymerase can use double-stranded DNA as a primer. The evidence so far available (86), indicates that the DNA separates into single strands before polymer synthesis takes place. Both transfer-RNA (97) and the messenger-RNA (88) are synthesized by DNA-dependent RNA polymerases.

5.7 Secondary structure of polynucleotides

Early X-ray crystallographic studies of DNA produced diffraction patterns characteristic of fibres and indications were obtained of periodicities in the fibres every 3·3 Å (89). The small periodicity of 3·3 Å between successive nucleotides was explained by the assumption that the flat nucleotides were stacked at right angles to the polymer chain.

Electrometric titration of DNA indicated that amino groups which were attached to the purines and pyrimidines did not titrate in a 'normal' fashion. This could mean that these groups were masked by internal hydrogen bonding in the polymer (90).

The ratios of adenine + thymine to guanine + cytosine is approximately unity for most samples of DNA (91). This ratio of base pairs together with additional X-ray crystallographic data led Watson and Crick to propose that specific pairs of bases in DNA were joined by hydrogen bonds (adenine to thymine, guanine to cytosine).

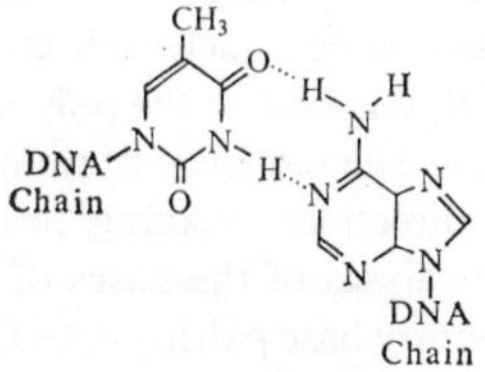

Adenine-thymine base pairing 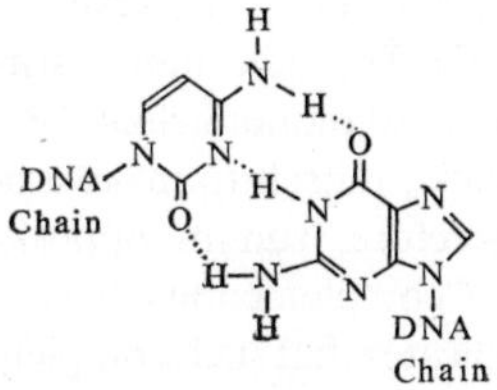   Guanine-cytosine base pairing

9

Watson and Crick proposed that DNA consists of two poly-nucleotide helices which were held together by hydrogen bonds between the purine and pyrimidine base pairs (12). The backbone sugar-phosphate chain is on the periphery of each helix and is parallel to the fibre axis, in contrast to the flat purine and pyrimidine bases which lie perpendicular to the fibre axis. Each polynucleotide helix is

coiled about the same axis in a right-handed manner with ten nucleotides per turn (34 Å) and the two helices have a diameter of 20 Å. The inter-nucleotide linkages run in opposite directions in the two chains. In the schematic drawing below, the ribbons represent the polynucleotide chains and the rods represent hydrogen bonds between the specific base pairs in the different chains.

DNA can exist in three forms which give rise to different diffraction patterns. The three forms differ mainly in the degree of twist (pitch) of the twin helices, a minor alteration to the Watson and Crick theory (92).

The X-ray diffraction pattern of a 1:1 complex of poly A and poly U is similar to that of DNA (76) and the complex has ten nucleotide residues per turn of the helix. X-ray diffraction patterns of other synthetic homopolynucleotides also show character-

Watson and Crick double helix

istics which are due to their possessing a helical conformation (93).

The diffraction patterns obtained from RNA fibres have a broad similarity to those obtained from DNA fibres but are too diffuse to be interpreted unequivocally (94). Crystalline yeast amino acid transfer-RNA does, however, yield an interpretable diffraction pattern (95). The molecule consists of one polynucleotide chain made up of about 80 mononucleotides with one-half of the polynucleotide folded back on itself to make a helix. The sequence of mononucleo-tides, therefore, run in opposite directions, making possible the pairing of complementary bases. Analyses of the bases of transfer-RNA indicates that such complementary base pairing does take place to a large extent. The 'extra' 2′ hydroxyl of the ribose moiety may be a stabilizing factor in this structure, and could form a hydrogen bond with either the ring oxygen of another ribose moiety or a hydroxyl of a phosphodiester group.

The molecule is about 100 Å long, and contains roughly $3\frac{1}{2}$ turns of the helix. It is probable that at least three nucleotides are accommodated in the 'bend' and these three nucleotides could be used as a

code of a RNA template (messenger-RNA) during protein synthesis. The occurrence of uncommon nucleotides, such as pseudouridylic acid, in the 'bend' could account for the specificity of sequence of amino acids in a protein, as the code of the transfer-RNA would specifically match a position of the code of the template (messenger-RNA).

There is no X-ray crystallographic evidence concerning the structure of the single-stranded DNA from bacteriophage ϕX174. However, its configuration in solution appears to be very dependent in the ionic strength, indicating that the DNA is flexible and that it can adopt different conformations depending on its ionic environment (96).

Transfer-RNA

Denaturing of a polynucleotide (for example by heat or by chemical means) leads to a change in the secondary structure from an ordered helical conformation to a random form in which the polymer strands are separate and coiled. The transition from a helix to a random form can be very sudden, which suggests that a definite denaturation process takes place, as opposed to a gradual, non-specific breaking down of the helix. If the DNA is assumed to have a totally ordered structure, this transition from order to disorder could take place by the 'unzipping' of the molecule from one end of the chain. Alternatively, the production of randomly unbonded regions at intervals in the DNA chain could disrupt the secondary structure sufficiently to produce the random structure. In a polynucleotide which does not possess a perfect helical structure, the transition from order to disorder is a gradual one and probably takes place by the 'unzipping' of small helical sections in the general macromolecular structure.

5.8 RNA and protein biosynthesis

This subject is in a considerable state of flux at the present time and fresh evidence concerning the mechanism of protein biosynthesis is being produced at a very rapid rate. However, an attempt has been made here to summarize some of the experimental evidence and interpretations concerning the role of RNA in protein biosynthesis.

Cells which are synthesizing protein contain relatively large amounts of RNA (97), and crude preparations of amino acid activating enzymes from liver contain a low molecular weight RNA which becomes labelled when ^{14}C-labelled amino acids are present in the system (98, 99). When these crude enzyme preparations were purified it was found that, in addition to catalysing the activation of amino acids by the formation of amino acyl-AMP derivatives, the enzymes also catalysed the transfer of amino acids to the low molecular weight RNA (transfer-RNA) which then played an integral part in the biosynthesis of proteins in all living organisms (100, 101).

From the stability of amino acyl transfer-RNA towards metaperiodate (102), and from the isolation of 2′(3′) amino acyl adenosine from a ribonuclease digest of amino acyl transfer-RNA (103), it was deduced that the amino residue was attached to either the 2′ or the 3′ hydroxyl group of the terminal nucleoside of transfer-RNA. The last three nucleotides at the 'acceptor' end of transfer-RNA are pCpCpA. This has been deduced by the successive incorporation of CTP, CTP, then ATP into transfer-RNA by the RNA polymerase (104) and from the degradation of unesterified transfer-RNA with metaperiodate followed by base (16). The amino acyl transfer-RNAs are formed *in vivo* by the acylation of the 2′(3′) hydroxyl of the terminal adenosine moiety by an activated amino acid which is a mixed anhydride of the amino acid and AMP.

In the majority of transfer-RNAs, the 'non acceptor' end of the polynucleotide chain ends in pGp (105). The complementary base to guanine in the Watson–Crick hypothesis is cytosine, so this may mean that base pairing, with concomitant helix formation, could begin at the third nucleotide from the 'acceptor' end of transfer-RNA. However, some pAp end grouping has been found in transfer-RNA from yeast, and this together with the isolation of pGpCp as the terminal dinucleotide in a large number of cases, casts doubt on base pairing beginning so close to the 'acceptor' end of transfer-RNA. The predominant base for the fourth nucleotide from the 'acceptor' end is adenine (106), which is not the complementary base for cytosine, so a stable helix is unlikely.

The determination of the exact location of the amino acyl residue on the terminal adenosine nucleoside is rendered difficult by the rapid interconversion of 2′ and the 3′ amino acyl adenosine derivatives in neutral or acid solution (107). 2′-Acetyl nucleosides are more susceptible than the 3′ isomers towards base catalysed solvolysis

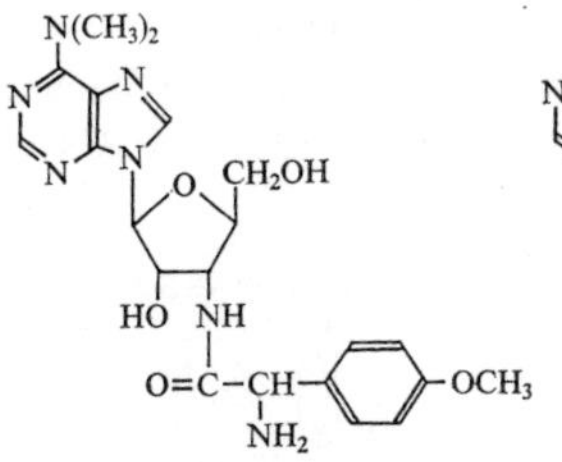

(VIII) 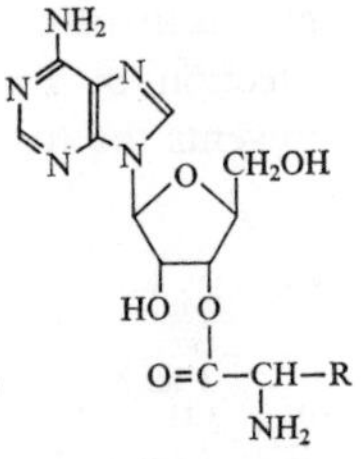   (IX)

(108), and hence the carbonyl group of 2′-amino acyl transfer-RNAs would appear to be the more readily attacked by an amino group of an 'incoming' transfer-RNA. However, this does not exclude the possibility that the amino acid may be initially attached to the terminal 3′ hydroxyl of the transfer-RNA and is then transferred to the more reactive 2′ hydroxyl group before peptide synthesis takes place. On the other hand puromycin inhibits protein synthesis in a wide variety of organisms (109). Puromycin (VIII) is an adenosine derivative which resembles 3′-amino acyl adenosine (IX), and it is postulated that the inhibition of protein synthesis by puromycin is due to its incorporation as the terminal nucleoside at the acceptor end of transfer-RNA. As the 3′ position would then be blocked by an 'unnatural' amino acid, protein synthesis cannot proceed.

If the amino group of one amino acyl transfer-RNA attacks the electrophilic carbonyl group of the second amino acyl transfer-RNA, peptidyl transfer-RNA is produced and the peptide chain can grow by a series of analogous reactions. Thus the peptide chain grows away from the amino group of the first amino acid, which becomes the N-terminal amino acid of the resulting polypeptide. The electrophilicity of the carbonyl group attached to the adenosine moiety is possibly increased by the formation of an internal hydrogen bond between the adjacent hydroxyl group of the adenosine nucleoside and the oxygen atom of the carbonyl group. This would facilitate the attack by the amino group of an amino acyl transfer-RNA (110).

The production of peptidyl transfer-RNA and the ultimate synthesis of protein takes place on aggregates of ribonucleoprotein known as ribosomes, and it appears that another type of RNA (messenger-RNA) is involved in this process.

Although infection of *Escherichia Coli* with bacteriophage T_2 immediately prevents the further net synthesis of RNA by the cell,

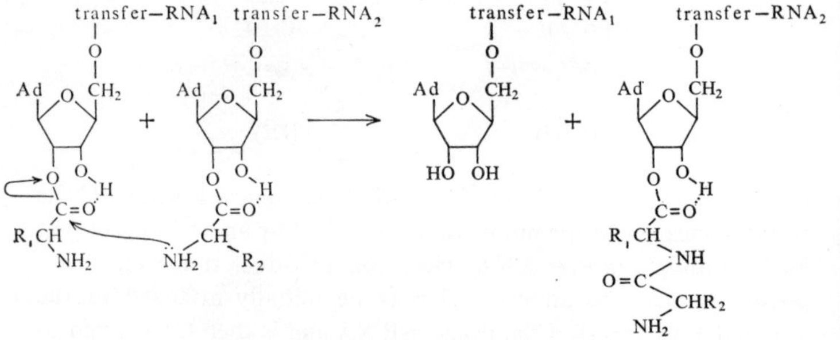

^{32}P-labelled orthophosphate is still incorporated into RNA and there is a rapid turnover of a small fraction of the total RNA of the cell (111). This RNA has a similar base composition to DNA and it appears that the phage DNA is transcribed into a template (messenger-RNA) in the host cell in order that the phage may replicate.

Messenger-RNA appears on stable ribosomes which had been formed before the infection of the cell with the bacteriophage (112), and uninfected cells of *E. Coli* contain an RNA which is rapidly synthesized and broken down by the cell (113) with a base composition similar to DNA (allowing for the substitution of uracil for thymine). Thus the ribosomes seem to be inactive carriers of messenger-RNA which is synthesized using the DNA of the cell nucleus as a template.

Ribosomes can aggregate into clusters (polysomes) in which the individual ribosomes are joined by single strands of messenger-RNA (114). The single-stranded RNA is hydrolysed by ribonuclease and very low concentrations of this enzyme degrade the polysomes into single ribosomal units (115).

Protein synthesis is believed to take place on transfer-RNA which is attached to the single-stranded messenger-RNA joining the ribosomes (116). It is proposed that the ribosomes carrying amino acyl transfer-RNA become attached by hydrogen bonds to one end of the messenger-RNA chain and then gradually move along the chain with the peptide chain of the peptidyl transfer-RNA growing all the time. When the ribosomes reach the end of the messenger-RNA chain, the polypeptide is detached from the transfer-RNA and the ribosomes, which now bear transfer-RNAs with free hydroxyl groups, can participate once more in protein synthesis. The nucleotides in the 'bend' of the transfer-RNA can code with successive sets of nucleotides on the messenger-RNA as the ribosome moves along the chain, so that only one amino acid is incorporated into a given position in the protein (117).

The rapid turnover of messenger-RNA (111) necessitates the rapid breakdown of the RNA, and the polysome theory for protein synthesis can account for this phenomenon. A small proportion of ribosomes contain ribonuclease present in a 'latent' form (118), and this ribonuclease could degrade the messenger-RNA chain as the ribosome advanced along the chain.

It can be seen that these theories shed some light on the problems associated with protein synthesis *in vivo*. However, it is apparent that much additional experimental work is necessary before the mechanism of protein biosynthesis is finally clarified.

REFERENCES

1. BROWN and TODD (1952), *JCS*, 52.
2. LEVENE and HARRIS (1933), *JBC*, **101**, 419.
3. COHN (1950), *JACS*, **72**, 2811.
4. BROWN and TODD (1952), *JCS*, 44.
5. COHN and VOLKIN (1951), *Nature*, **167**, 483.
6. COHN and VOLKIN (1953), *JBC*, **203**, 319.
7. CHARGAFF (1942), *JBC*, **144**, 455.
8. BAILLY and GAUME (1935), *Bull. Soc. Chim.*, **2**, 354.
9. BROWN, MAGRATH, and TODD (1952), *JCS*, 2708.
10. ELMORE and TODD (1952), *JCS*, 3681.
11. BROWN, HEPPEL, and HILMOE (1954), *JCS*, 40.
12. WATSON and CRICK (1953), *Nature*, **171**, 964.
13. SANGER (1959), *Science*, **129**, 1340.
14. WHITFELD (1954), *BJ*, **58**, 390.
15. BROWN, FRIED, and TODD (1955), *JCS*, 2206.
16. YU and ZAMECNIK (1960), *BBA*, **45**, 148.
17. MOSS, REESE, SCHOFIELD, SHAPIRO, and TODD (1963), *JCS*, 1149.
18. VIZSOLYI and TENER (1962), *Chem. & Ind.*, 263.
19. TAMM, HODES, and CHARGAFF (1952), *JCS*, **195**, 49.
20. BURTON and PETERSEN (1957), *BBA*, **26**, 667.
21. DISCHE (1930), *Mikrochemie*, **8**, 4.
22. BURTON (1956), *BJ*, **62**, 315.
23. BIRKHOFER and DUTZ (1962), *Annalen*, **657**, 94.
24. HALL and SINSHEIMER (1963), *J. Mol. Biol.*, **6**, 114.
25. LEVENE and BASS (1926), *JBC*, **41**, 167.
26. BARON and BROWN (1955), *JCS*, 2855.
27. HABERMANN (1962), *BBA*, **55**, 999.
28. VERWOERD and ZILLIG (1963), *BBA*, **68**, 484.
29. COHN and VOLKIN (1957), *BBA*, **24**, 359.
30. MARKHAM and SMITH (1952), *BJ*, **52**, 558.
31. RUSHIZKY and SOBER (1962), *JBC*, **237**, 2883.
32. VOLKIN and COHN (1953), *JBC*, **205**, 767.
33. BROWN and TODD (1953), *JCS*, 2040.
34. HEPPEL, ORTIZ, and OCHOA (1956), *Science*, **123**, 415.
35. MCDONALD (1955), *Methods in Enzymol.*, **2**, 437.
36. SINSHEIMER (1954), *JBC*, **208**, 445.
37. RALPH, SMITH, and KHORANA (1962), *Biochem.*, **1**, 131.
38. SHIMOMURA and LASKOWSKI (1957), *BBA*, **26**, 197.
39. KOERNER and SINSHEIMER (1957), *JBC*, **228**, 1039.

40. HODES and SWENSON (1962), *BBA*, **61**, 612.
41. VANECKO and LASKOWSKI (1962), *BBA*, **61**, 547.
42. RAZZELL and KHORANA (1959), *JBC*, **234**, 2105.
43. TURNER and KHORANA (1959), *JACS*, **81**, 4651.
44. PRIVAT DE GARHILE and LASKOWSKI (1956), *JBC*, **223**, 661.
45. RAZZELL and KHORANA (1961), *JBC*, **236**, 1144.
46. HEPPEL and RABINOWITZ (1958), *Ann. Rev. Biochem.*, **27**, 613.
47. GULLAND and SMITH (1948), *JCS*, 1532.
48. HALL, TODD, and WEBB (1957), *JCS*, 3291.
49. CORBY, KENNER, and TODD (1952), *JCS*, 3669.
50. MICHELSON and TODD (1955), *JCS*, 2632.
51. KHORANA (1961), *Some recent developments in the chemistry of phosphate esters of biological interest*, Wiley, N.Y.
52. GILHAM and KHORANA (1958), *JACS*, **80**, 6212.
53. TENER (1961), *JACS*, **83**, 159.
54. GILHAM and KHORANA (1959), *JACS*, **81**, 4647.
55. RAMMLER, LAPIDOT, and KHORANA (1963), *JACS*, **85**, 1989.
56. WEIMANN and KHORANA (1962), *JACS*, **84**, 4329.
57. GRUNBERG-MANAGO and OCHOA (1955), *JACS*, **77**, 3165.
58. BESSMAN, LEHMAN, SIMMS, and KORNBERG (1958), *JBC*, **233**, 171.
59. MICHELSON (1963), *The Chemistry of Nucleosides and Nucleotides*, Academic Press, London, Chapter 7.
60. KHORANA and VIZSOLYI (1961), *JACS*, **83**, 675.
61. KHORANA, VIZSOLYI, and RALPH (1962), *JACS*, **84**, 414.
62. SCHALLER, WEIMANN, and KHORANA (1963), *JACS*, **85**, 355.
63. UKITA, BATES, and CARTER (1955), *JBC*, **216**, 867.
64. MICHELSON (1959), *JCS*, 1371.
65. MICHELSON and LETTERS (1962), *JCS*, 71.
66. MICHELSON (1959), *JCS*, 3655.
67. KORNBERG (1957), *Adv. in Enzymol.*, **18**, 191.
68. GRUNBERG-MANAGO and OCHOA (1955), *Fed. Proc.*, **14**, 221.
69. LITTAUER and KORNBERG (1957), *JBC*, **226**, 1077.
70. BEERS (1957), *BJ*, **66**, 686.
71. GRUNBERG-MANAGO, ORTIZ, and OCHOA (1956), *BBA*, **20**, 269.
72. ORTIZ and OCHOA (1959), *JBC*, **234**, 1208.
73. GRIFFIN, TODD, and RICH (1958), *PNAS*, **44**, 1123,
74. SASSE, RABINOWITZ, and GOLDBERG (1963), *BBA*, **72**, 353.
75. GRUNBERG-MANAGO (1961), *The Enzymes*, **5**, 257.
76. RICH (1957), *The Chemical Basis of Heredity*, eds. McElroy and Glass, Johns Hopkins, Baltimore, p. 557.
77. MII and OCHOA (1957), *BBA*, **26**, 445.

78. SINGER, HEPPEL, and HILMOE (1957), *BBA*, **26**, 447.
79. SINGER, HEPPEL, and HILMOE (1960), *JBC*, **235**, 738.
80. SINGER (1958), *JBC*, **232**, 211.
81. SINGER, HILMOE, and GRUNBERG-MANAGO (1960), *JBC*, **235**, 2705.
82. KORNBERG (1960), *Science*, **131**, 1503.
83. BOLLUM (1963), *Prog. in Nucleic Acid Research*, **1**, 1.
84. BOLLUM (1962), *JBC*, **237**, 1945.
85. GRUNBERG-MANAGO (1962), *Adv. in Biochem.*, **31**, 301.
86. HURWITZ and AUGUST (1963), *Prog. in Nucleic Acid Research*, **1**, 59.
87. CHIPCHASE and BIRNSTIEL (1963), *PNAS*, **49**, 692.
88. COHEN, SEIKIGUCHI, STERN, and BARNER (1963), *PNAS*, **49**, 699.
89. ASTBURY and BELL (1938), *Nature*, **141**, 747.
90. GULLAND and JORDAN (1947), *Symposium Soc. Exptl. Biol.*, **1**, 56.
91. CHARGAFF (1955), *The Nucleic Acids*, eds. Chargaff and Davidson, Academic Press, N.Y., Vol. I, p. 350.
92. LANGRIDGE, WILSON, HOOPER, WILKINS, and HAMILTON (1961), *J. Mol. Biol.*, **3**, 547.
93. LANGRIDGE and RICH (1963), *Nature*, **198**, 725.
94. WATSON and RICH (1954), *Nature*, **173**, 995.
95. SPENCER, FULLER, WILKINS, and BROWN (1962), *Nature*, **194**, 1014.
96. SINSHEIMER (1959), *J. Mol. Biol.*, **1**, 41.
97. BRACHET (1955), *The Nucleic Acids*, eds. Chargaff and Davidson, Academic Press, N.Y., Vol. II, p. 476.
98. HOAGLAND, ZAMECNIK, and STEPHENSON (1957), *BBA*, **24**, 215.
99. HOAGLAND, STEPHENSON, SCOTT, HECHT, and ZAMECNIK (1958), *JBC*, **231**, 241.
100. OSAWA (1960), *BBA*, **43**, 110.
101. TISSIERES (1959), *J. Mol. Biol.*, **1**, 365.
102. HECHT, STEPHENSON, and ZAMECNIK (1959), *PNAS*, **45**, 505.
103. ZACHAU, ACS, and LIPMANN (1958), *PNAS*, **44**, 885.
104. HECHT, ZAMECNIK, STEPHENSON, and SCOTT (1958), *JBC*, **233**, 954.
105. RALPH, YOUNG, and KHORANA (1963), *JACS*, **85**, 2002.
106. BERG, LAGERKUIST, and DIECKMANN (1962), *J. Mol. Biol.*, **5**, 159.
107. RAMMLER and KHORANA (1963), *JACS*, **85**, 1997.
108. CLARK, JOHNSTON, and SUGINOME, unpublished results.
109. NATHANS and NEIDLE (1963), *Nature*, **197**, 1076.
110. ZAMECNIK (1962), *BJ*, **85**, 257.
111. ASTRACHAN and VOLKIN (1958), *BBA*, **29**, 536.
112. BRENNER, JACOB, and MESELSON (1961), *Nature*, **190**, 576.

113. GROS, HIATT, GILBERT, KURLAND, RISEBOROUGH, and WATSON (1961), *Nature*, **190**, 581.

114. WARNER, RICH, and HALL (1962), *Science*, **138**, 1399.

115. WARNER, KNOPF, and RICH (1963), *PNAS*, **49**, 122.

116. GOODMAN and RICH (1963), *Nature*, **199**, 318.

117. WATSON (1963), *Science*, **140**, 17.

118. NOLL, STAEHELIN, and WETTSTEIN (1963), *Nature*, **198**, 632.

Index

DATE

261-2500

Printed in USA